WELDED HIGHWAY
BRIDGE DESIGN

Editor

James G. Clark

Professor of Civil Engineering

University of Illinois

Price $2.00

This book may be ordered direct from

THE JAMES F. LINCOLN ARC WELDING FOUNDATION

Cleveland 17, Ohio

PREFACE

The number of welded highway bridges is steadily increasing, but the rate of increase should be even greater. The lack of adequate information on the design of welded bridges in the books now available is partially responsible for the insufficient number of welded bridges in this country.

As a means of stimulating structural designers to make new discoveries employing new concepts of economy, performance, and beauty in the design of welded bridges, the James F. Lincoln Arc Welding Foundation sponsored two award programs entitled "Welded Bridges of the Future"—the first program in 1949 and the second in 1950. The participants in these two programs did contribute valuable ideas in the designs and details of their bridges. The more important material of the 1949 program was presented in *Welded Deck Highway Bridges* published by the Foundation in 1950. Similarly, *Welded Highway Bridge Design* contains information from the 1950 program.

All of the designs of the 1950 programs were similar to the extent that they satisfied the requirement of the Rules and Conditions that each exhibit be an original, all-welded design for a two-lane through highway bridge with a span of 250 feet. However, the designs varied considerably in the type of primary structure and in the kind of floor system used. They differed also in the arrangement and make-up of individual members and in the details of the connections.

Because it is impracticable to publish all of the many designs submitted, this book contains a selection of the material, made with the intention of discussing the major features of enough designs to insure that most of the new and important ideas would be included. There are numerous cases where similar ideas were presented in more than one design, but to conserve space for other new and useful information, only one of such design is mentioned.

By dividing the book into chapters and the chapters into further divisions or classifications, it is easier to compare structural types that are similar, floor systems that are similar, etc. Such an advantage justifies this arrangement, but simultaneously it necessitates the discussion of some designs in more than one chapter. In these instances where a design is mentioned a second or third time, reference is made to the previous discussion.

James G. Clark

Urbana, Illinois

March, 1952

Published by
The James F. Lincoln Arc Welding Foundation
First Printing, October, 1952

DEDICATED TO

THE HIGHWAY BRIDGE ENGINEERS

Who through their perseverance and intuition and through research have made it possible for our highways to cross natural and other barriers by means of structures known as bridges.

They hold safety for human lives foremost, but at the same time have sought economy by applying the latest principles of design and construction. The use of welding in steel bridges is one of these measures of economy with safety which has been applied to their designs. Their progress in this field is worthy of note.

Raymond Archibald

Chairman, Bridge Committee,

American Association State Highway Officials

U. S. Bureau of Public Roads

CONTENTS

CHAPTER I

INTRODUCTION

The James F. Lincoln Arc Welding Foundation

From the time it was established in 1936, The James F. Lincoln Arc Welding Foundation has sponsored many programs. These programs have differed greatly both in size and scope. Three of them have been $200,000 Award Programs, general in nature, and including many fields. The Annual Engineering Undergraduate Award and Scholarship Programs have likewise been rather broad and general; however, some of the other programs have been more specialized, two of which were entitled "Welded Bridges of the Future" and conducted in 1949 and 1950. For the Foundation, these two were both unique in that each was limited to designs of a specified structure.

All of the programs, as well as the other activities, of the Lincoln Foundation have satisfied the following requirement from its Deed of Trust,

"The object and purpose of The James F. Lincoln Arc Welding Foundation is to encourage and stimulate scientific interest in, and scientific study, research and education in respect of the development of the arc welding industry through advance in knowledge of design and practical application of the arc welding process."

The Trustees of the Foundation have followed the policy of making available to the public some of the valuable information presented in their programs, and accordingly, approved the publication of this book which is restricted to the "Welded Bridges of the Future, 1950 Award Program."

The Trustees and Officers of the Foundation are:

Trustees:
E. E. Dreese, Chairman, Columbus, Ohio
H. R. Harris, Cleveland, Ohio
T. V. Koykka, Cleveland, Ohio
Officers:
A. F. Davis, Secretary, Cleveland, Ohio
C. G. Herbruck, Assistant Secretary, Cleveland, Ohio

The Award Programs for Design of Bridges

This 1950 Award Program and the 1949 Award Program were similar. The purpose of both was to stimulate original and creative thinking in highway bridge design. Unlike other programs sponsored by the Foundation, each of these limited the participants to the design of a specific structure.

The structure to be designed for the 1949 Award Program was described as follows: "A two-lane deck highway bridge supported on two end piers 120 feet apart, center line to center line of bearings." Since *Welded Deck Highway Bridges,* published by the Foundation in 1950, describes this earlier program and includes much of the data of the designs presented therein, this book will be devoted solely to the 1950 Award Program.

According to the 1950 Rules and Conditions, each participant was to present an original, all-welded design for a bridge of the following description:

A Two-Lane Through Highway Bridge With a Span of 250 Feet.

To be in accordance with common bridge design practice and in order that the designs submitted would be more competitive, specifications for the two-lane through highway bridge were given in the Rules and Conditions. These specifications were as follows:

Controlling Dimensions

Span: 250 feet, center line to center line of bearings. Between the abutments at each end there shall be no intermediate support. There shall be no adjacent spans. Temporary falsework may be used during erection.

Roadway: 26 feet wide, inside face to inside face of curbs. There shall be no median strip or barrier between the two traffic lanes.

Curbs: At least 1' - 6" wide from inside face of curb to inside face of railing. There shall be one such curb on each side of the roadway.

Railings: There shall be railings on each side of the bridge and these railings shall lie inside of the main structure. The clear distance, inside to inside of railings, shall be not less than 29 feet.

Vertical Clearance: For the entire 26-foot roadway width, 14 feet of vertical clearance shall be provided between the top of the roadway surface and the bottom of any overhead structure.

Floor and Curbs: The roadway floor and curbs may be made of any material or combination of materials suitable for the purpose.

Type of Bridge: The type of bridge may be: truss, arch, tied arch, or any other feasible type of structure.

Abutments

Inasmuch as the design of the substructure is not included in this competition, the participant may assume that suitable abutments are available. However, he shall show the outline of the upper parts or other essential portions of the abutments in the general drawings (plans, sections and elevations) of the superstructure.

Design of Superstructure

In order that exhibits shall be competitive, it is necessary that they comply with certain additional mandatory requirements, as follows:

The bridge shall be designed for ASTM-A7-46 steel. The requirements for base metal specifications are published in Appendix E of the 1947 edition of the Standard Specifications for Welded Highway and Railway Bridges of the American Welding Society.

Base Stress: Axial tension on net section—18,000 pounds per square inch.

Dead Load: The dead load shall consist of the weight of the superstructure complete, including all structural steel, roadway floor, curbs, and railings.

Live Load: Two types of loading shall be considered, (a) standard truck and (b) lane loading. The type of loading to be used shall be that which produces maximum stress in any member.

For purposes of load computation, each standard truck or lane loading shall be considered to occupy a traffic lane, 10 feet wide. The roadway shall be considered as consisting of two traveled lanes 13 feet wide. One traffic lane load shall be applied to each 13-foot width so placed as to produce the greatest stress. Fractional truck loads or fractional widths of lane loads shall not be considered.

The standard truck loading shall consist of the following load concentrations: 1 front axle of 8,000 lbs. (4,000 lbs. per wheel), and 1 rear axle of 32,000 lbs. (16,000 lbs. per wheel); distance between axles—14 feet; distance between centers of wheels on the same axle—6 feet.

The lane loading shall consist of a uniform load of 640 lbs. per lineal foot of traffic lane combined with a single concentrated load, both so placed on the span, longitudinally and transversely, to produce maximum stress. The concentrated load shall have a value of 18,000 lbs. for moment and 26,000 lbs. for shear. Both the uniform load and concentrated load shall be considered as uniformly distributed over the 10-foot width of traffic lane, normal to center line of roadway.

The impact load allowance shall be that fraction of the live load stress determined by the formula:

$$I = \frac{50}{L + 125} \text{ but not to exceed 30 per cent, in which L is}$$

the length in feet of the portion of the span which is loaded to produce the maximum stress in the member.

The wind force on the structure shall be assumed as a moving horizontal load equal to 30 lbs. per sq. ft. on 1½ times the area of the structure as seen in elevation, including the floor system and railings.

The lateral force due to the moving live load shall be 200 lbs. per linear foot and shall be considered as acting 6 feet above the roadway.

Structures designed for these lateral forces in combination with dead load, live load and impact forces may be proportioned for the normal unit stresses increased by 25 per cent. However, the resulting sections shall not be less than those required for dead load, live load and impact at the normal unit stresses.

Any type of floor adequately attached to its supports may be assumed to act as the web system in resisting the lateral forces specified above.

A floor which serves only as such and does not participate in the strength of the supporting structure shall be designed only so far as is necessary to indicate the dimensions from which the gross weight is determined. A floor which is designed to contribute to the strength of the supporting structure shall be designed in sufficient detail to indicate the extent and manner of its participation.

The exhibit shall include the allowable unit stresses which were used in the design of this floor, if it is not of steel.

While the above requirements are mandatory, certain other specifications in common use should be followed as a guide by the participant. These are:

The 1949 edition of the American Association of State Highway Officials Standard Specifications for Highway Bridges and the 1947 edition of the Standard Specifications for Welded Highway and Railway Bridges of the American Welding Society.

While adherence to the two listed specifications is not mandatory, any divergence from them in the preparation of an exhibit should be justified and explained by the participant. Departures from the specifications are encouraged where, but only where, it is felt that such departures are a significant contribution to the evolution of these specifications.

The mandatory specifications were intentionally very brief—sufficient only to define the size, the base stress, the live load, and the impact—because the evolution of bridge specifications must go hand in hand with the evolution of bridge design. Furthermore, the designs were not limited by present structural steel shapes or traditional methods and facilities for fabrication. In fact, the participants were encouraged to incorporate new sections provided the design could be improved thereby and that the shape could be readily produced if a sufficient demand were to develop.

In rating the merits of the exhibits, the Jury of Award gave consideration to the following factors:

1. Compliance with the "Specifications" as given above.
2. The ingenuity exercised in developing shapes, arrangement of individual members, sections and connections that can readily be assembled and welded in both shop fabrication and field erection, with due regard to methods possible in existing and future fabricating shops.
3. The cost, including maintenance.
4. Probable life.
5. The appearance of the bridge.

A discussion in clear concise English was required in addition to the general drawings, detail drawings, and tabulations of steel quantities and lengths of welds. All of this must have been completely executed within the period of the competition, November 1, 1949 to June 30, 1950. Exhibits had to represent the work of the designer or designers submitting them, but they could be based on the previous studies, experiences, and thinking of the designers.

This program was dedicated to Professor Wilbur M. Wilson who conceived this and the 1949 bridge program and presented them to the Trustees of the Foundation for their approval.

The Chairman of the Rules Committee and the Jury of Award selected men of recognized qualifications who collectively would represent highway bridge engineers, steel fabricators, consulting engineers, and university professors with practical experience. The Rules Committee and Jury of Award together included the following:

Wilbur M. Wilson—Honorary Chairman
Research Professor of Structural Engineering
University of Illinois
Urbana, Illinois

Professor James G. Clark—Chairman
Department of Civil Engineering
University of Illinois
Urbana, Illinois

Professor E. E. Dreese
Chairman, Board of Trustees, Lincoln Foundation
Chairman, Department of Electrical Engineering
The Ohio State University, Columbus, Ohio

Mr. Raymond Archibald
Chairman, AASHO Bridge Committee
U. S. Bureau of Public Roads
Washington, D. C.

Mr. Harry C. Boardman
Director of Research
Chicago Bridge and Iron Company
Chicago, Illinois

Mr. Shortridge Hardesty, Consulting Engineer
Hardesty and Hanover
New York, New York

Mr. John I. Parcel, Consulting Engineer
Sverdrup and Parcel
St. Louis, Missouri

Mr. Lee E. Philbrook
Assistant Bridge Engineer
Illinois State Division of Highways
Springfield, Illinois

Professor Frank W. Stubbs, Jr.
School of Civil Engineering and Engineering Mechanics
Purdue University
Lafayette, Indiana

The Jury of Award comprised all of the men above except Messrs. Hardesty and Philbrook who were unable to be present at the time of the judging.

The 1950 Awards

Every member of this Jury examined each of the exhibits individually, prior to the studies and discussions of the combined jury. This method of judging was consistent with the extreme precautions taken by the Officers of the Foundation to assure that each exhibit should receive fair and proper consideration as well as confidential handling.

After the rating of the exhibits had been completed by the Jury of Award, the exhibits were returned to the Office of the Foundation where the identity of the author of each exhibit was determined by comparing the unidentified copy used for judging with its signed, original paper on file with the Secretary of the Foundation. Notification of awards were sent to the entrants and an announcement of the awards was made in various trade and technical journals.

A total of $10,750 was paid to the authors of the thirteen designs which received awards. A list of the award winners with a very brief description of each is as follows:

First Award—$5000

James H. Jennison, 1612 Coolidge Avenue, Pasadena 7, California.
Design—A tied arch with a rise of 45 feet at the center line, 13 panels, and stiffening tie girders. Arch ribs are 14 WF, hangers and K bracing are 8-in. or 6-in. pipe.

Second Award—$2500

Ernst Amstutz, Hardturmstrasse 74, Zurich, Switzerland.
Design—Two-hinged arch with a slender rib and a single stiffening girder of semi-cylindrical shape located at the center of the roadway.

Third Award—$1250

Thomas C. Kavanagh, Department of Civil Engineering, Pennsylvania State College, State College, Pennsylvania.
Design—Tied arch with arch ribs tilted and sloped toward each other so that a single member is thus used over the center 40 ft. of the arch. Stiffening girders act as ties and are inclined to correspond to tilt of rib.

Ten Honorable Mention Awards—$200 each

J. R. Daymond, and M. S. Zakrzewski, both of University of Natal, Howard College, Durban, South Africa.
Design—A two-hinged arch for which the thrust is taken by props extending from the abutments. Rectangular, air-tight arch ribs braced laterally with stiff transverse struts at the panel points.

Arsham Amirikian, 6526 Western Avenue, Chevy Chase 15, Maryland.
Design—A wedge-beam Vierendeel truss, 23 ft. deep, having 10 panels. Many duplicate parts in main truss simplify fabrication.

John E. Kayser, c/o James Brunton, 15 Passaic Avenue, Roseland, New Jersey.
Design—Curved chord Pratt truss of 10 panels with center depth of 35 ft. Each truss member consists of two tees welded either to a web plate or to tie plates, but in every case forming a special I shape.

E. R. Bretscher; and J. W. Briscoe, both of 201 Civil Engineering Hall, University of Illinois, Urbana, Illinois.

Design—A tied arch with 8 panels and a rise of 64 ft. at the center. Each rib composed of 4 extra strong 6-in. pipes, two vertical webs, one cover plate, and one bottom perforated plate.

Wlodzimierz Gorgolewski, 31, West Hill, Wembley, Mddx., England; and Kazimierz Lecewicz, 16, Champion Grove, London, S. E. 5, England.
Design—Tied arch with light arch ribs stiffened by 2 girders, each a closed trapezoidal box section, spaced 13 ft. - 4 in. apart beneath the roadway. These girders are a substantial part of the roadway system and serve as the ties, being attached to the arch ribs by a horizontal truss at each end.

A. A. Brielmaier, 2511 Hampton Avenue, St. Louis 10, Missouri; and John A. DeLong, 3921 Pennsylvania Avenue, St. Louis 18, Missouri.
Design—A three-hinged arch with a rise of 37 ft. - 6 in. and stiffening girders used as ties. Hangers every 50 ft. Floorbeams every 25 ft. frame into tie girders. New tees and channels for flanges of girders and floorbeams and for rib, respectively.

John Turner Percy, Department of Civil Engineering, Rensselaer Polytechnic Institute, Troy, New York.
Design—Two-hinged tied arch with 9 panels. A crescent shaped truss for the arch. Standard WF sections used for arch truss, main tie, floor steel, and bracing.

Sidney Rochlin, 4147 Holly Knoll Drive, Los Angeles 27, California.
Design—A 10 panel, modified Pratt truss with top chord horizontal over middle 4 panels. Truss members are WF sections with no gussets at connections.

I. L. Hamilton, 2 Laughland Drive, Newarthell, Lanarkshire, Scotland.
Design—Two-hinged tied arch with heavy stiffening, tie girders which are unsymmetrical about their vertical axes. Arch ribs are closed boxes composed of 4 plates each.

K. W. Dobert, 786 Third Avenue, Troy, New York.
Design—A fixed arch of 16 panels having rectangular arch ribs that come close together between the portals, being braced at hanger points by large struts. Hangers are inclined. They connect to curved brackets attached to floorbeams.

More elaborate descriptions and discussions of these designs, in addition to some of their drawings, are given in the chapters which follow. These award winners are only thirteen of the many good designs entered in this program.

Summary of the Designs

This program was very successful, considering both the number and quality of the designs. The participants have recognized ability and many are outstanding structural engineers who are well-known professionally. The authors represent 20 states in this country and 16 other countries. They include consulting engineers, bridge engineers of state highway departments, structural engineers with governmental organizations, designers of steel fabricating companies, structural engineers of research organizations, and professors of structural engineering.

Designs for a structure such as the one specified for this program involve a great deal of work, but an extremely high percentage of them are complete, well designed, and original. They incorporate the high caliber and experiences of the authors and much creative thinking. Some of the new ideas in the many good designs are excellent, and will undoubtedly influence future structural design. The new shapes proposed provided a saving in fabrication costs and a decrease in weight by permitting a more efficient distribution of areas. The form of these new sections indicates that many steel shapes in production today might be materially different if welding had been the only fabricating process known when these shapes were being standardized.

In some designs, the planes of the arches are inclined, thus reducing the amount of top lateral bracing to a very small fraction of what is usually necessary. The inclined connections and, for some, the trapezoidal ribs and ties which result are simple for welded fabrication. Also the welded connections for the highly efficient circular sections used in many designs are not complicated. Participants emphasized that rolled setions could be produced with the edges shaped to further decrease the fabrication costs for these connections, and that beveled edges would frequently be of benefit to normal connections.

Some of the designers proportioned the ties of their arch bridges to serve also as stiffening girders. Other designers have the longitudinal members of the floor system, or a steel floor plate, or both act as the arch ties. Participating floor slabs or plates are not limited to the arch bridges. Many floor plates and some slabs function simultaneously as the structural roadway and one or more of the following: the bottom lateral bracing, a part of the bottom chord of the main trusses, the top flanges of stringers, and the top flanges of floorbeams.

The following chapters contain discussions and descriptions of many of the exhibits presented in this program. Numerous drawings are reproduced there to provide the maximum amount of detail information. The selection of the designs and the drawings to be included is based upon the desire to publish the information of greatest value to the most readers. Unquestionably, the designers would agree that their designs could be improved by spending more time and effort, that in eliminating certain expensive details and connections others have increased slightly in cost, and that perfection is never reached— just more closely approached. However, by publishing this material, bridge designers will be able to add to their present knowledge some information that will result in better bridges of the future.

Patents

As stated in the Rules and Conditions of this Program, "The Foundation is not and will not be interested financially in any patent rights of designs submitted, nor will the existence of such patents in any way affect the rating of the exhibit by the Jury." However, information about patents and patent applications was required to enable the Foundation to properly refer any inquiries concerning the use of the design.

Some parts of a few of the designs presented in the following chapters are subject to patent rights or a patent has been applied for them. For these designs, the information concerning the patents will be contained in the figures and drawings or in the discussions of the designs.

CHAPTER II

STRUCTURAL TYPES

The designers who entered exhibits in this program used many different types of structures for the principal members of their bridges. Because of these variations and to permit easier comparisons, the basic structural types are divided into six classifications. A few of the designs could be logically placed in either of two classifications; for an example, two-hinged, tied arches with inclined hangers are included in "Other Arched Structures" although they could have been included in "Two-Hinged Arches" even though structurally they are not the same as normal two-hinged arches with vertical hangers.

This chapter contains discussions of only a limited number of the designs submitted, and it does not include all of the information given in any one design. Except for suspension bridges, the material presented here gives the basic data from at least one of every type of bridge entered in this program. The order in which the designs are discussed has no relationship to the number or quality of the exhibits. Reference is made to some designs which one or more of the jurors did not believe entirely satisfied all of the specifications of the published Rules and Conditions.

Two-Hinged Arches

Of all the various types of bridges represented, the two-hinged arch is the most numerous. It is used as the primary structure in slightly more than a third of the total number of designs. Most of the two-hinged arches are tied, and these will be described first—followed by those that have the abutments resist the longitudinal thrust of the arch. Approximately half of the arch bridges have stiffening girders and somewhat flexible arch ribs. Almost all of the arch ribs have solid webs, with only a few having relatively shallow trusses with parallel chords; however, two are crescent arches.

By inclining the two arch ribs toward each other, two designers have a single arch member throughout the middle portion of the bridge span. Another designer has only one stiffening girder of semi-circular shape located along the center line of the bridge. The utilization of a participating floor system to function as the tie, the stiffening girders, or the bottom lateral bracing is an important part of some of the designs.

Because this classification includes so many designs—more than any other classification—it is divided into three parts.

11

Two-Hinged Arches
A. *With Ties and Stiffening Members*

Except for a very few, the designers of this type of bridge employed a stiffening girder to act as both the tie and the stiffening member for a flexible arch rib. The exceptions include the use of a floor plate for the tie, the use of a truss in place of a stiffening girder, and the use of a relatively rigid floor system as both the tie and stiffening member.

James H. Jennison, Pasadena, California, designed the tied arch shown in Figure 1. The tie serves also as a stiffening girder which carries 97 per cent of the total moment at the several panel points while the slender arch rib carries only 3 to 4 per cent.

The arch rib is made up of a series of chords with the panel points on a parabola having a rise of 45 ft. Concerning this, Mr. Jennison stated: "This rise is in favorable proportion to the span from the standpoint of economy and of appearance. The panel lengths, 1 at 15 ft., 11 at 20 ft., 1 at 15 ft., were chosen primarily for economy in the floor system, but the layout is also a good one for the tied arch design." He prefers the segmental rib because it is somewhat easier to fabricate than a curved rib would be. The rib varies from a 14 WF 167 at the hinges to 14 WF 136 at the center of the span.

The tie girder has a 60-in. web plate and 18-in. flange plates. Because it is necessary to attach the hangers to the top flange, it is designed to a stress of 13,500 lb. per sq. in. (75 per cent of the basic 18,000 lb. per sq. in.), but the bottom flange is "designed to the full basic stress, as it has no stress-raising attachments welded to it." Consequently, the top plates are thicker than the bottom plates making the girder unsymmetrical about a horizontal axis and placing the center of gravity approximately 6 in. above mid-depth. For this reason, the working line is 6 in. above the center of the girder. Also, the girder is cambered a total of 6 in. The computed maximum moments, both positive and negative, in the tie girder are corrected for the effect of this camber, and the girder is proportioned for both these corrected moments and the direct tension at the various points along the span.

In discussing the girder web, the author said: "Although the shear stresses in the web of the tie girder are low, a careful investigation of these stresses was made. Influence lines for girder shear were used to obtain the shear at critical points.

"The longitudinal tension stress in the girder web proved to be of considerable benefit in increasing the elastic stability of the girder web against buckling caused by shear. The ⅜-in. web plate meets the requirement for minimum thickness of web plates for plate girders, specified as not less than ¹⁄₁₇₀ of the depth between flanges [see *Standard Specifications for Highway Bridges*, American Association of State Highway Officials, Fifth Edition, Art. 3.6.75, 1949]. However, the A.A.S.H.O. specifications for stiffener spacing on plate girders is not applicable [see Art. 3.6.80 of reference above]. The elastic stability of the web under the action of the combined tension and shear stress was thoroughly investigated, using formulas developed by Timoshenko [S. Timoshenko, *Theory of Elastic Stability,* McGraw-Hill Book Company, pp. 357-363, 1936] and the National Advisory Committee for Aeronautics [O. S. Heck and H. Ebner, *Methods and Formulas for Calculating the Strength of Plate and Shell Constructions as Used in Airplane Design,* National Advisory Committee for Aeronautics, Tech. Memo. 785, Feb. 1936] ....:

"The tension stress in the tie girder web increases the stability of the web enough that the ⅜-in. web plate has a factor of safety of 5 against buckling, although no stiffeners are used. The web is made ½ in. thick in the end panels because of local shear stress at the end bearings. At all panel points, the web is stiffened by the split pipe sections which transfer the concentrated floorbeam loads through the girder to the hangers. The absence of stiffeners except at panel points simplifies the girder fabrication, reduces cost, saves steel, makes painting easier, and gives a pleasing, clean appearance to the girder.

"Welded stiffeners of the conventional type, made from plate, are provided at the ends of the tie girder to transmit the concentrated loads from the arch rib and the end bearings. The ends of these stiffeners are milled and welded only where they transmit direct compressive load."

Mr. Jennison chose pipe for the hangers because of the advantages which he gave as follows:

1. The radius of gyration is the same about all axes and is greater than that of any other section of equal weight.

2. The member selected to give the limiting $\frac{L}{r}$ of 200 provides more than enough cross-sectional area for the load carried.

3. The pipe hangers can be used as posts to support the arch rib during erection.

4. There is less surface requiring painting than there would be on an equivalent built-up section or wide flange section, and the absence of edges makes painting easier, and the paint job will be more durable.

5. Pipe gives a more substantial appearance than would be presented by more slender hanger rods.

6. The cylindrical surface is smooth and esthetically attractive.

7. The vertical lines of the hangers are accented by using split pipe for rib and girder web stiffeners at the panel points.

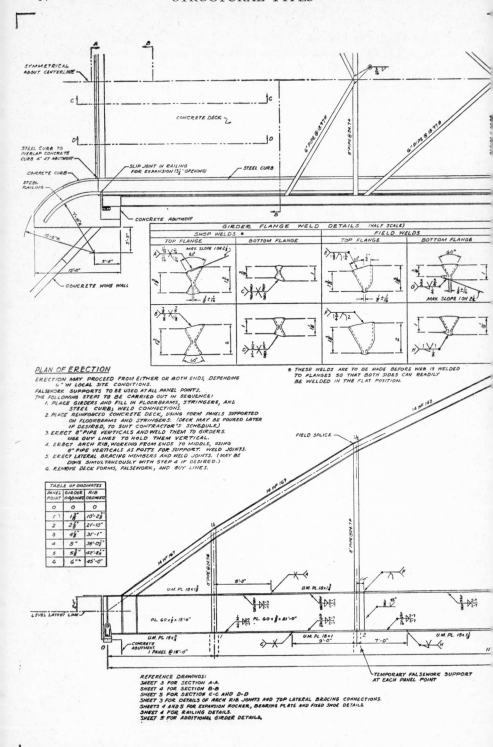

Figure 1

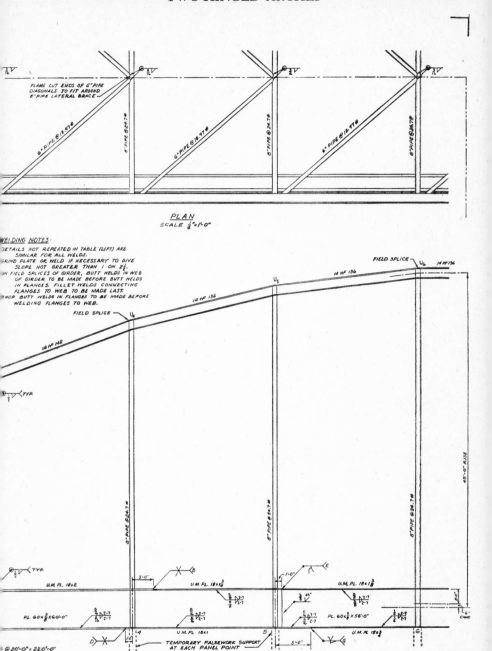

PLAN
SCALE ¼"=1'-0"

WELDING NOTES:
DETAILS NOT REPEATED IN TABLE (LEFT) ARE
SIMILAR FOR ALL WELDS.
GRIND PLATE OR WELD IF NECESSARY TO GIVE
SLOPE NOT GREATER THAN 1 ON 2½.
ON FIELD SPLICES OF GIRDER, BUTT WELDS IN WEB
OF GIRDER TO BE MADE BEFORE BUTT WELDS
IN FLANGES. FILLET WELDS CONNECTING
FLANGES TO WEB TO BE MADE LAST.
SHOP BUTT WELDS IN FLANGES TO BE MADE BEFORE
WELDING FLANGES TO WEB.

ELEVATION

8" PIPE HANGERS TO BE SEAMLESS OR RESISTANCE-WELDED
BLACK PIPE, GRADE B, ASTM DESIGNATION A53-47

Figure 1 (Concluded)

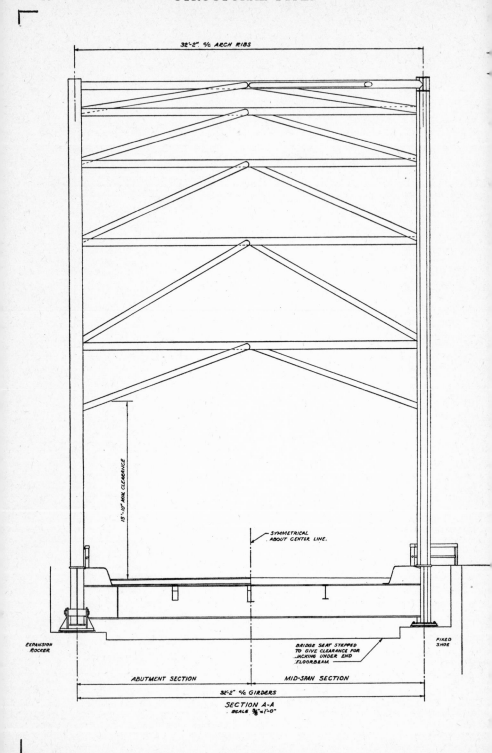

Figure 2

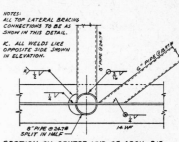

NOTES:
ALL TOP LATERAL BRACING CONNECTIONS TO BE AS SHOW IN THIS DETAIL.

K. ALL WELDS LIKE OPPOSITE SIDE SHOWN IN ELEVATION.

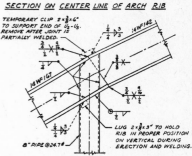

TYPICAL BUTT WELD
FULL SIZE

14 WF 167

PORTAL BRACE CONNECTION

SECTION ON CENTER LINE OF ARCH RIB

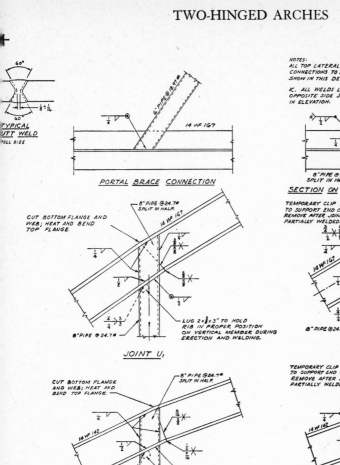

CUT BOTTOM FLANGE AND WEB; HEAT AND BEND TOP FLANGE.

8" PIPE @ 24.7# SPLIT IN HALF.

14 WF 167

LUG 2×⅜×3" TO HOLD RIB IN PROPER POSITION ON VERTICAL MEMBER DURING ERECTION AND WELDING.

8" PIPE @ 24.7#

JOINT U₁

TEMPORARY CLIP 2×⅜×6" TO SUPPORT END OF U₂-U₃. REMOVE AFTER JOINT IS PARTIALLY WELDED.

14 WF 142

14 WF 167

8" PIPE @ 24.7#

LUG 2×⅜×3" TO HOLD RIB IN PROPER POSITION ON VERTICAL DURING ERECTION AND WELDING.

JOINT U₂

CUT BOTTOM FLANGE AND WEB; HEAT AND BEND TOP FLANGE.

8" PIPE @ 24.7# SPLIT IN HALF.

14 WF 142

8" PIPE @ 24.7#

LUG 2×⅜×3" TO HOLD RIB IN PROPER POSITION ON VERTICAL MEMBER DURING ERECTION AND WELDING.

JOINT U₃

TEMPORARY CLIP 2×⅜×6" TO SUPPORT END OF U₄-U₅. REMOVE AFTER JOINT IS PARTIALLY WELDED.

14 WF 136

14 WF 142

8" PIPE @ 24.7# SPLIT IN HALF.

8" PIPE @ 24.7#

LUG 2×⅜×3" TO HOLD RIB IN PROPER POSITION ON VERTICAL MEMBER DURING ERECTION AND WELDING.

JOINT U₄

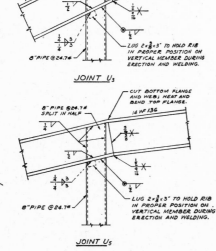

CUT BOTTOM FLANGE AND WEB; HEAT AND BEND TOP FLANGE.

8" PIPE @ 24.7# SPLIT IN HALF.

14 WF 136

8" PIPE @ 24.7#

LUG 2×⅜×3" TO HOLD RIB IN PROPER POSITION ON VERTICAL MEMBER DURING ERECTION AND WELDING.

JOINT U₅

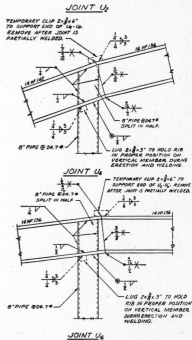

8" PIPE @ 24.7# SPLIT IN HALF.

TEMPORARY CLIP 2×⅜×6" TO SUPPORT END OF U₅-U₆. REMOVE AFTER JOINT IS PARTIALLY WELDED.

14 WF 136

8" PIPE @ 24.7#

LUG 2×⅜×3" TO HOLD RIB IN PROPER POSITION ON VERTICAL MEMBER DURING ERECTION AND WELDING.

JOINT U₆

ARCH RIB JOINT DETAILS
SCALE 1" = 1'-0"

GENERAL NOTES:-
WELDS IN WF SECTION OF RIB TO BE MADE AND INSPECTED BEFORE WELDING 8" PIPE STIFFENERS EXCEPT AT JOINTS U₆ AND U₆'. WEBS TO BE WELDED BEFORE FLANGES.

ALL-WELDED THROUGH HIGHWAY BRIDGE		
TRANSVERSE SECTION AND ARCH RIB JOINTS		
DATE 4-31-50	SCALE - NOTED	SHEET 3 OF 5

Figure 2 (Concluded)

About the lateral bracing, he said: "The lateral bracing between the arch ribs was arranged as a K truss to give the diagonals minimum length. Pipe is used for all lateral bracing members, because the sizes of these members are governed by limiting $\dfrac{L}{r}$ values rather than by stress. Pipe is an ideal section for such light members because of its large radius of gyration and symmetry. The ends of the pipes can be flame cut to the desired shape. The fillet welds used are more than adequate; they are made continuous to seal the pipes against entrance of moisture."

Details of some of these connections are shown in Figure 2. The reinforced concrete deck and the floor system are discussed in Chapter III and the shoes in Chapter V. Drawings of the floor system and shoes are reproduced as Figures 66 and 100, respectively.

Thomas C. Kavanagh, State College, Pennsylvania, presented an unusual tied arch bridge which has the arch planes tilted so that a single rib section is common to both arches throughout the middle portion of the span. The stiffening girders, acting also as ties, have the same inclination as the arches. Figure 3 shows the inclined arches about which the author gave the following remarks:

"The inclination of the arch planes, as incorporated in the design submitted, accomplishes the following structural functions:

1. It eliminates about 80 to 90 per cent of the top bracing. (A current growing interest in pony truss bridges indicates a desire on the part of engineers here to dispense with much of the overhead maze which has characterized so many through bridges in the past).
2. There is no reduction in rigidity of the arches, because they are arched in plan and brace each other directly, without relying upon the interaction with a secondary (bracing) system.
3. For the center ribs where the arches are of common section, some economy is effected by virtue of the fact that eccentric lane loadings need not be considered for these members.
4. Some economy is possible due to interaction of the lower bracing system (the floor grid) with the tie girder under vertical loadings, tending to reduce the axial load in the latter under eccentric lane loadings.

"The arch itself is self-anchored; it requires no massive abutments to take its thrust, and thus is suited for many locations for which ordinary two-hinged arches might not be suited.

"The ribs are of box shape, comparable on a reduced scale to the sections used on the St. Georges span, and very similar in design to the sections successfully employed on the Swedish welded railway arch previously cited [C. T. Ingwall, 'Arc Welding in Steel Structures in Sweden', *International Association for Bridge and Structural Engineers, Preliminary Publication 3rd Congress,* Liege, p. 75, 1948]. As in the latter design, batten plates are used on the underside of the rib, and the hangers are connected to special rib plates at the panel points. The arch is curved throughout, and of parabolic shape.

"The analysis of this type of structure is accomplished by methods similar to those described by Professor J. M. Garrelts [J. M. Garrelts, 'Design of the St. Georges Tied Arch Span', *Trans. ASCE,* No. 108, Vol. 69, p. 543, 1943], or found in standard European treatises [see Bibliography, pp. 422-424 of *Statically Indeterminate Structures,* J. I. Parcel and G. A. Maney, John Wiley and Sons, New York, Second Edition, 1936], such as in the works of Mueller-Breslau or of the late F. Bleich. The design includes modification according to the flitch-beam concept by virtue of which a small portion of the girder moment is absorbed by the rib."

Figure 4 shows the rib sections, the girder sections, and the influence lines for girder moments and rib thrusts. The tie girders have horizontal flange plates (16 in. wide) welded to inclined webs (72 in. by ½ in.) and are stiffened by ordinary plate stiffeners except at the panel points where split WF sections are used.

The hangers are wire rope (1¼-in. Galvanized Bridge Strand) if wire rope is permitted; otherwise, welded H sections (two 6 x ¼ flanges and one 6 x ¼ perforated web). In regard to these hangers, Mr. Kavanagh said: "These strands will be taut under dead load, and by virtue of their lightness have a calculated sag which is negligible under any conditions of loading."

The floor system, which consists of a diagonal gridwork of WF beams and takes the place of the lower lateral bracing, will be discussed in Chapter III.

Wlodzimierz Gorgolewski, Wembley, Middlesex, England, and Kazimierz Lecewicz, London, England, described their bridge in the following manner:

"The submitted design consists of flexible light arch ribs with connected rigid stiffening girders. These stiffening girders serve also as ties to the arch ribs. The main new feature in the design as compared with existing bridges of this type of construction is the positioning of the stiffening girders out of the planes of the arch ribs, right underneath the roadway; the load is thus carried out in the most direct way and the adopted box shape of the stiffening girders allows them to take over the role of longitudinal girders (stringers) of the floor system as well.

"The horizontal thrust exerted by both arch ribs is transferred and

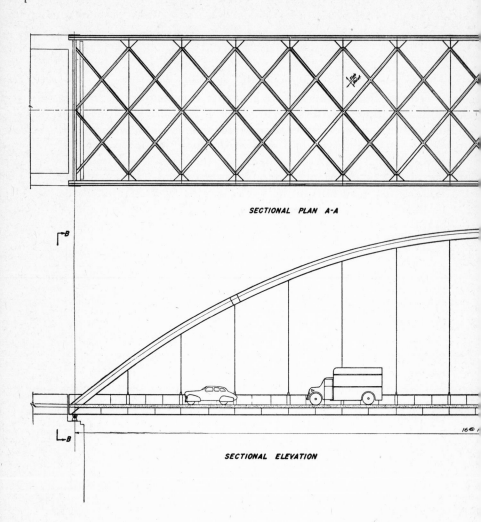

SECTIONAL PLAN A-A

SECTIONAL ELEVATION

DATA:
    H 20 LOADING
    ASTM A-7-46 STEEL
    AASHO 1949 SPECS. FOR HWY. BRIDGES
    AWS 1947 SPECS. FOR WELDED BRIDGES

DRAWINGS:
    1. PLANS & ELEVATIONS
    2. ISOMETRIC OF FLOOR SYSTEM
    3. STRESSES & DETAILS
    4. DETAILS

Figure 3

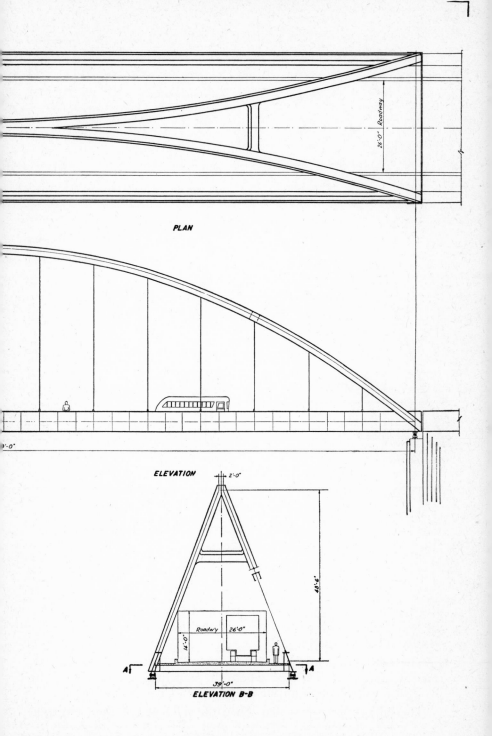

PLAN

ELEVATION

ELEVATION B-B

Figure 3 (Concluded)

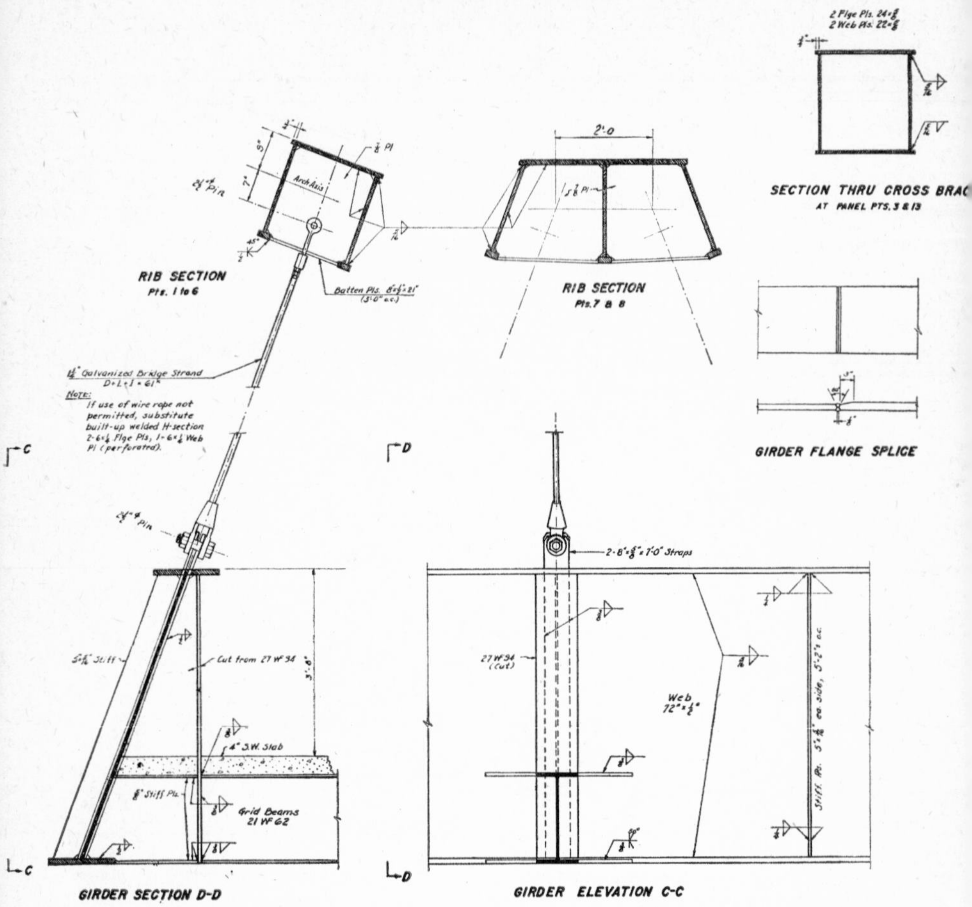

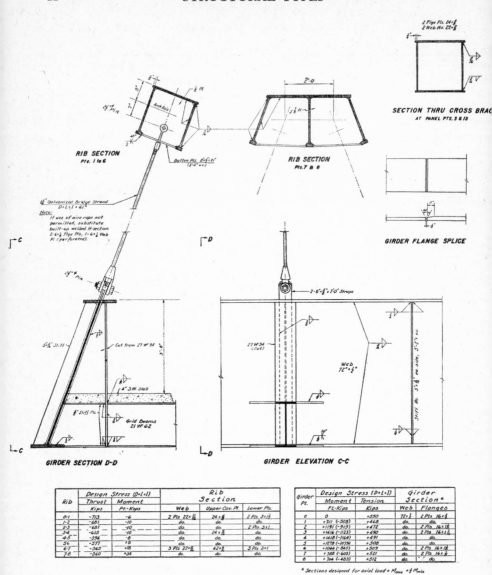

Rib	Design Stress (D+L+I)		Rib Section		
	Thrust	Moment			
	Kips	Ft.-Kips	Web	Upper Cov. Pl.	Lower Pls.
0-1	-713	-6	2 Pls 22×11/16	24×5/8	2 Pls 3×1¼
1-2	-681	-10	do.	do.	do.
2-3	-681	-10	do.	do.	2 Pls. 3×1
3-4	-615	-10	do.	24×9/16	do.
4-5	-594	-8	do.	do.	do.
5-6	-577	+8	do.	do.	do.
6-7	-565	+18	3 Pls 22×11/16	42×9/16	3 Pls 3×1
7-8	-560	+34	do.	do.	do.

Girder Pt.	Design Stress (D+L+I)		Girder Section*	
	Moment	Tension		
	Ft.-Kips	Kips	Web	Flanges
0	0	+550	72×½	2 Pls 16×¾
1	+711 (-508)	+468	do.	do.
2	+1191 (-915)	+472	do.	2 Pls 16×1⅛
3	+1416 (-1123)	+490	do.	2 Pls 16×1 7/16
4	+1418 (-1164)	+491	do.	do.
5	+1278 (-1073)	+508	do.	do.
6	+1044 (-845)	+509	do.	2 Pls 16×1⅛
7	+788 (-603)	+521	do.	2 Pls 16×⅞
8	+704 (-483)	+512	do.	" " do.

* Sections designed for axial load + M_{max} + ½ M_{min}

Figure 4

distributed by two suitable horizontal girders situated at both ends of the span to the entire cross section of the floor system, including the tubular stiffening girder.

"The span made up in this way does not differ essentially from existent bridges of this type where the stiffening girders lie in the plane of the arch ribs from the point of view of structural theory.

"The only difference is that when the influence of the elongation

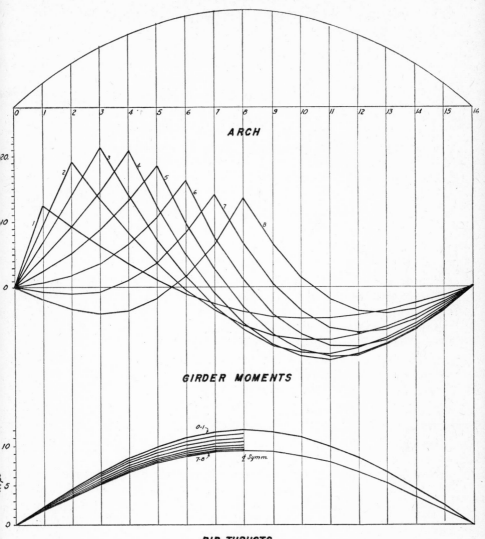

ARCH

GIRDER MOMENTS

RIB THRUSTS

INFLUENCE LINES
(1-Kip Load in Plane of the Arch)
Figure 4 (Concluded)

of the hangers on the stresses in the arch ribs is calculated—the deflections of the cantilevered parts of the cross beams must be added to the elongations of the hangers."

The authors point out that the merits of the design are both its economy in the weight of steel and its favorable appearance. They list the economies as:

1. The elimination of all intermediate stringers normally needed

to support the floor gives a saving of about 15 per cent in the weight of steel.

2. By positioning the stiffening girders right underneath the loading, bending moments and shear forces in the floorbeams are decreased by about 25 per cent.

3. The adopted shape of the cross section of the stiffening girder and its direct connection with the floor plate permits the use of working stresses in tension and in compression in the upper and lower plate as high as 18,000 lb. per sq. in. There is no need to consider buckling as would be necessary in any of the conventional cross sections.

4. The steel plate which supports the floor slab is stressed in a longitudinal and in a transverse direction. A very economical use of steel is attained as the whole cross section of the floor system can be assumed to participate in carrying the horizontal thrust and the bending moments.

From the standpoint of aesthetics, the authors state that heavy arch ribs are unfavorable, also that the thin light arch ribs generally do not harmonize with the rather bulky stiffening girder which is visible. In this design the stiffening girders are set back underneath the roadway; "in the foreground, apart from a light arch rib, one sees only a narrow longitudinal edge beam which supports the curb." The depth of the entire floor system is 4 ft.-8 in. or $\frac{1}{53}$ of the span length.

Figure 5 shows the elevation, the plan views, and the section views of the bridge and Figure 6 gives the details and connections.

The trapezoidal stiffening girders are 64 in. wide at the top, 52 in. deep, and 24 in. wide at the bottom. They are spaced 6 ft.-8 in. from the center line of the roadway. With the $\frac{5}{16}$-in. floor plate and its longitudinal stiffeners (ST6B), these box girders act as the arch ties. In the end panels, the floor plate is $\frac{5}{8}$ in. thick, and this thicker plate together with the floorbeams to which it is attached form a horizontal girder that distributes the longitudinal thrust from the arches to the stiffening girders. Details of the girders are shown with the details of the floor system in Chapter III.

The arch rib has a parabolic shape with a rise of 32 ft. It is a box section about 20 in. square made up of a top plate, two side plates, and two bottom square bars. The span of 250 ft. is divided into nine panels; the end panels being 27 ft. in length and the interior panels 28 ft. The ribs are braced with struts which in combination with the arch ribs form a Vierendeel truss five panels long.

The function of a lower wind bracing system is taken by the rigid reinforced concrete roadway slab acting jointly with the steel floor plates to which it is attached.

The hangers are made up of two round bars $1^{11}\!/_{16}$ in. in diameter. They are shop welded (see Figure 6) into single members that resemble the traditional forged connections.

Messrs. Gorgolewski and Lecewicz elaborate upon the saving in erection falsework and field work in general that is possible by the use of the box shape for the stiffening girders, also upon the favorable conditions of maintenance by having about 70 per cent of the steel underneath the bridge floor.

I. L. Hamilton, Newarthell, Lanarkshire, Scotland, designed a two-hinged arch with flexible arch ribs and stiff tie girders. The span is divided into ten panels. The arch rib is straight between panel points, but at the panel points, the arch axis coincides with a parabolic curve having a rise of 35 ft. at the center. The arch rib is composed of four plates arranged to form a rectangular section, 16 in. wide and 17 in. deep. Figure 7 includes an outline and sections of the arch, a cross section of the bridge, sections of the tie girder, and details of the floor system and rib connections. The tie girder is not symmetrical about a vertical axis; the web (60 in. by $\frac{3}{8}$ in.) is positioned to the outside of the center line of the 16-in. flange plates. The hangers consist of two, 6-inch channels connected by $\frac{1}{2}$-in. diameter lacing, giving them a 16-in. width.

The top lateral bracing is provided by struts which, with the vertical hangers and floorbeams, make up rectangular frames capable of taking the wind from the arch to the lower lateral bracing. The struts are rigidly attached to the arch ribs, and the hangers have rigid connections at both the arch above and the tie girder below.

Mr. Hamilton states that the strain energy theory may be applied to a parabolic tied arch with the following assumptions:

1. Hanger loads are all equal—i.e., stiffening girder is so stiff that variations in hanger loads, due to live load concentration, are small. This assumption leads to the polygonal parabolic arch which, for equal loads in hangers is then subjected only to direct compression. Tests on several bridges of this type have proved that no bending stresses of any serious nature are set up. This is probably due to the fact that the stiffness of the arch, not considered in the normal theory, helps to equalize hanger loads since combined resistance of arch and girder to vertical deflection is considerable.

2. The extension of hangers is neglected.

3. The dead load is taken totally by the arch ribs and bending stresses, in girder between panel points, are then taken as secondary stresses.

Also he states: "The bridge behaves as a suspension bridge with a very

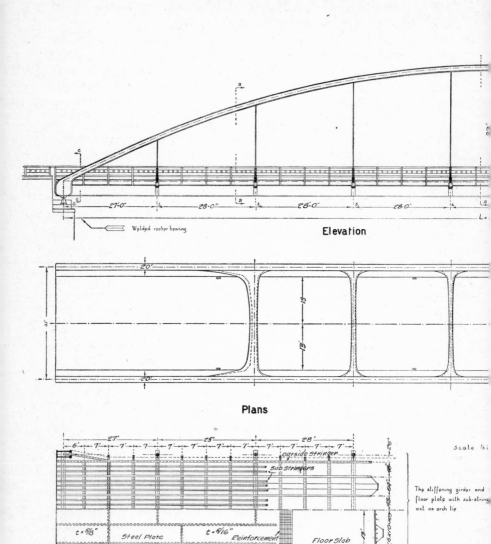

Welded rocker bearing

Elevation

Plans

outside stringer

sub stringers

The stiffening girder and
floor plate with sub-string-
act as arch tie

$t = \frac{5}{8}''$ Steel Plate $t = \frac{9}{16}''$ Reinforcement   Floor Slab

That thicker steel plate together
with the floor beams form the girder
to distribute the horizontal load.

Scale ½"

Figure 5

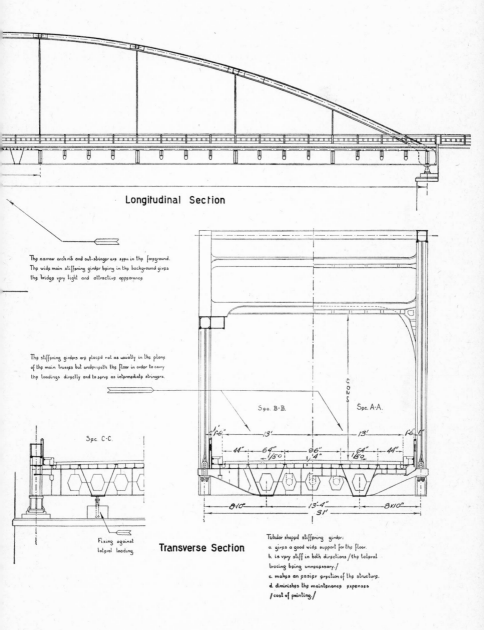

Longitudinal Section

The narrow arch rib and out-stringer are seen in the foreground. The wide main stiffening girder being in the background gives the bridge very light and attractive appearance.

The stiffening girders are placed not as usually in the plane of the main trusses but underneath the floor in order to carry the loadings directly and to serve as intermediate stringers.

Sec. B-B.

Sec. A-A.

Sec. C-C.

1'-6"   13'   13'   1'-6"

44"   64"   96"   64"   44"
1/50   1/50   1/4

8'10"   13'-4"   8'10"
31'

Fixing against lateral loading

Transverse Section

Tubular shaped stiffening girder:
a. gives a good wide support for the floor.
b. is very stiff in both directions (the lateral bracing being unnecessary.)
c. makes an easier erection of the structure.
d. diminishes the maintenance expenses (cost of painting.)

Figure 5 (Concluded)

ARCH RIB AND HANG

Sketch drawing of details.

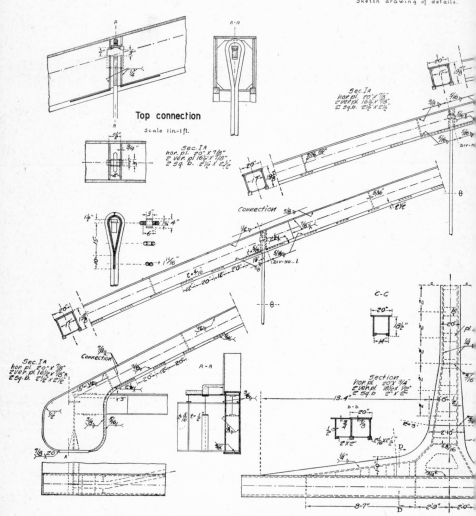

Top connection

Scale 1in-1ft.

Figure 6

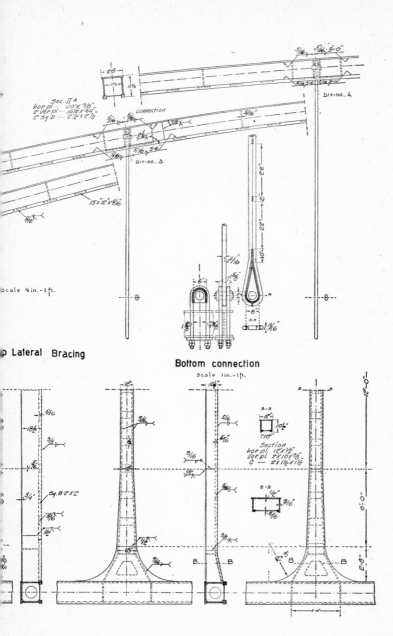

Bottom connection

Figure 6 (Concluded)

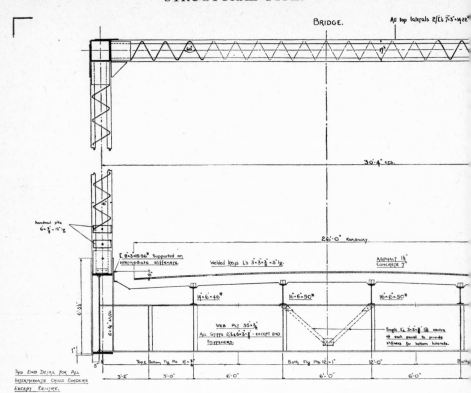

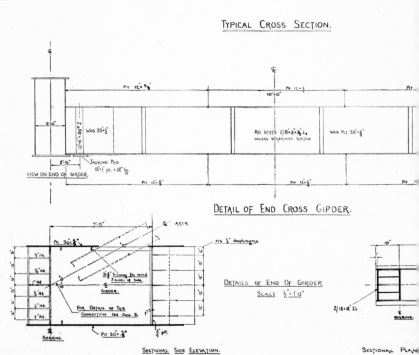

TYPICAL CROSS SECTION.

DETAIL OF END CROSS GIRDER.

DETAILS OF END OF GIRDER
SCALE ½"=1'0"

SECTIONAL SIDE ELEVATION.

SECTIONAL PLAN

Figure 7

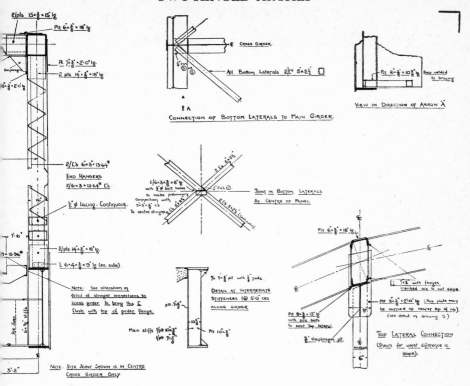

CONNECTION OF BOTTOM LATERALS TO MAIN GIRDER.

All Bottom Laterals 2/℄ 5 × 2½ □

VIEW IN DIRECTION OF ARROW "A"

JOINT IN BOTTOM LATERALS AT CENTRE OF PANEL

TOP LATERAL CONNECTION (Shown for worst difference in slope).

DETAIL AT INTERMEDIATE STIFFENERS (@ 5'-0" CRS ALONG GIRDER)

NOTE: See alteration in detail of stringer connections to cross girder to bring this ℄ flush with top of girder flange.

END HANGERS 2/℄ 6 × 3 × 13.64 ℄'s

NOTE. SITE JOINT SHOWN IS IN CENTRE CROSS GIRDER ONLY

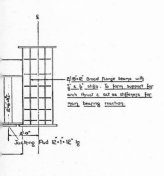

2/18 × 12 Broad Flange beams with ℄ ℄ stiffs. To form support for arch thrust & act as stiffeners for main bearing reaction.

Jacking Pad 12 × 1 × 12" lg

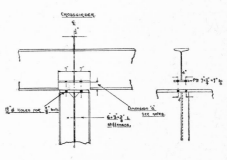

DETAIL OF STRINGER CONNECTION.

CROSS GIRDER

15/16 φ HOLES FOR bolts

6 × 3 × ½ ℄ stiffeners.

Dimension 'a' see notes.

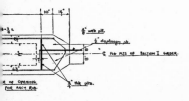

FOR DETAILS OF HANDRAIL SEE ATTACHED SKETCH.

GENERAL NOTES:

FOR WELDING DETAIL SEE DRAWING N°6.

BATTEN PLTS MAY BE USED ON HANGERS IF PREFERRED.

DIMENSION 'a' IS TO SUIT MAKING ℄ STRINGER FLUSH WITH GIRDER FLGE.

SITE LOCATION BOLTS NOT SHOWN ARE IN OBVIOUS POSITIONS.

ERECTION CLEATS ETC ARE INDICATED ON DRAWING 5 BUT FINAL POSITIONING IS LEFT TO THE CONTRACTOR.

ALL STEEL IS ASTM - A7 - 46.

DETAIL OF ARCH RIB CONNECTION TO GIRDER IS ON DRAWING N°3.

PLATES ETC REQD ON HANGERS TO ATTACH HANDRAILING ARE NOT SHOWN ON THIS DRAWING.

ALL STEELWORK IS TO BE SAND BLASTED AND SPRAYED WITH AN APPROVED METALLIC COMPOUND.

AN INSPECTION HOLE IS TO BE MADE IN SIDE OF GIRDER FOR MAINTENANCE OF ARCH BEARING.

Figure 7 (Continued)

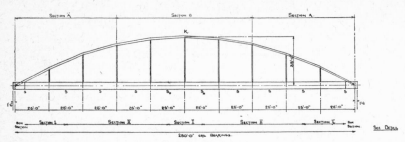

Key Diagram of Main Truss Members.

NOTES:
CAMBER OF 8" REQD AT CENTRE.
JOINTS IN GIRDER MARKED 'S'
JOINTS S₂ MADE WHEN BRIDGE
IS SUSPENDED.
JOINT 'K' IS ONLY SITE JOINT IN ARCH.

DETAILS OF SECTIONS:

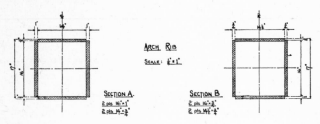

ARCH RIB

SCALE: ¼" = 1'

SECTION A.
2 pls 16"×1"
2 pls 14"×¾"

SECTION B.
2 pls 16"×¾"
2 pls 14½"×¾"

STIFFENING GIRDER.

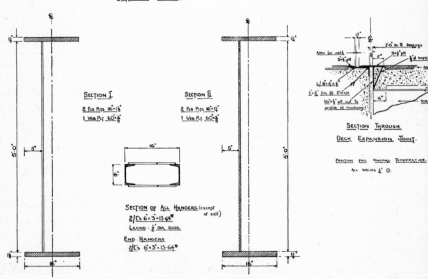

SECTION I
2 Flg Plts 16"×1⅛"
1 Web Plt 60"×⅜"

SECTION II
2 Flg Plts 16"×1½"
1 Web Plt 60"×⅜"

SECTION OF ALL HANGERS (except of end)
2/Cs 6"×3"×13.64#
LACING: ⅞" DIA RODS.

END HANGERS
2/Cs 6"×3"×13.64#

SECTION THROUGH
DECK EXPANSION JOINT.

POSITION FOR NORMAL TEMPERATURE.
ALL WELDS ¼" ①

Figure 7 (Concluded)

stiff girder and a compression member taking the place of the cable tension."

Hermann Ehrlich, Vlissingen, Holland, calls his stiffened tied arch a "Plate-Girder with Arch-Chord." The radius of the arch-chord is 207 ft.-4¼ in., giving it a rise of 41 ft. The roadway has a rise of 1:125. There are eleven panels, the end panels being shorter (22 ft.-7½ in.) than the nine center panels (22 ft.-9 in.). The arch rib has a 19¾-in. cover plate, two web plates 24 in. deep, and two bottom flats 4¾ in. wide. The webs are 14 in. apart. The heavy stiffening tie girders are 96½ in. deep, and are made up of ST 18 WF 130 flanges welded to a 60½-in. web plate. The web plates are ⅝ in. thick except near the ends where the thickness is ⅞ in. Portals located at the first panel point are rigid frames. The top lateral bracing between portals is composed of double intersecting diagonals without lateral struts. Each of the diagonals consists of two, 5-in. pipes spaced one foot apart vertically by welding stay plates between them. Tees are used for the bottom lateral bracing. The hangers are 3-in. rods. Figures 8 and 9 show the details of the rib, girder, bracing, and hangers.

Arick S. Malkiel, Philadelphia, Pennsylvania, used a rigid "Roadway Plate" as the tie and the stiffening member for his two-hinged arched bridge. The arch ribs are 14 WF sections (103 to 127 lb. per ft.) of parabolic shape and have a rise of approximately 38 ft. at the center of the span. The span is divided into ten panels of equal length. The top lateral system has struts (12 WF 53) and intersecting diagonals (10 WF 33). Each hanger consists of four angles connected by stay plates to form an I shape. Figure 10 shows the elevation and plan view of this bridge.

Considering the "Roadway Plate" as a single unit, the entire structure including the floor system is composed of the arch ribs, the top lateral bracing, the hangers, and the "Roadway Plate". At the ends, the "Roadway Plate" increases in width, as shown in Figure 11, to permit it to function as the tie for the arch ribs. Essentially, the "Roadway Plate" is a floor plate stiffened both longitudinally and transversely by space trusses for which the plate itself is the top chords. In a longitudinal direction, the unit serves as stringers as well as the stiffening member for the arch ribs. A cross section of the bridge and of the new proposed sections are shown in Figure 12. Details of the connections for the rib and "Roadway Plate" are given in Figures 11 and 12, and Chapter III contains a discussion of the floor system.

Mr. Malkiel retains all rights to patent any and all parts of this design.

Amulf Arild, Oslo, Norway, gave the following description of his design:

"The bridge is designed as a tied flexible arch with stiffening truss.

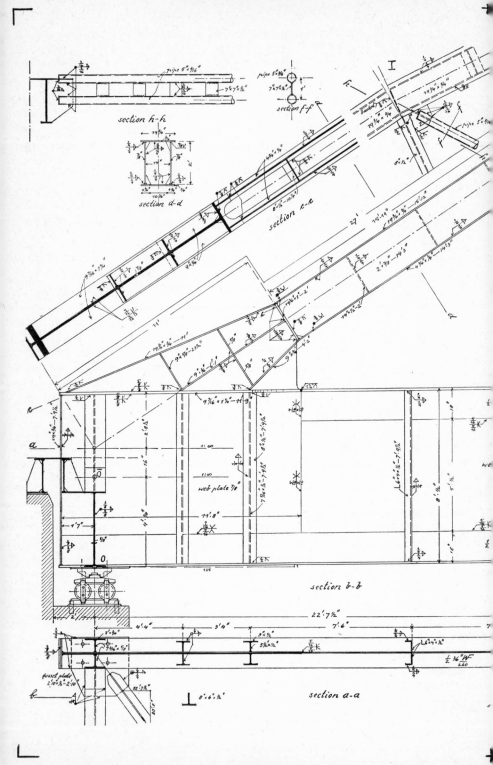

Figure 8

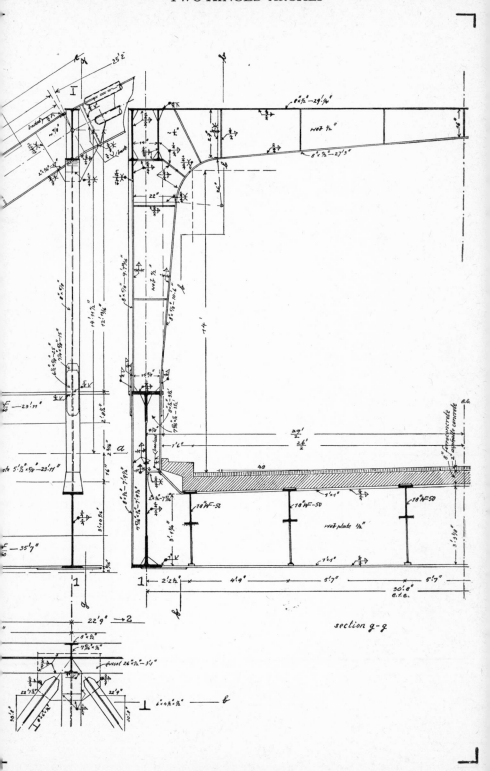

section g-g

Figure 8 (Concluded)

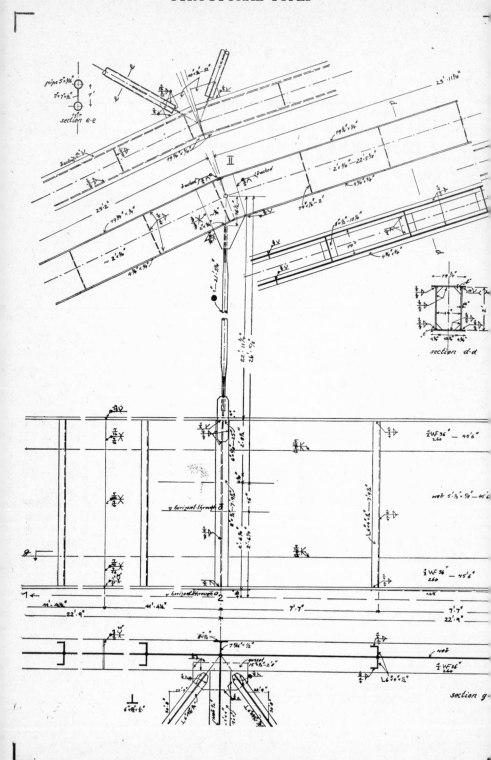

Figure 9

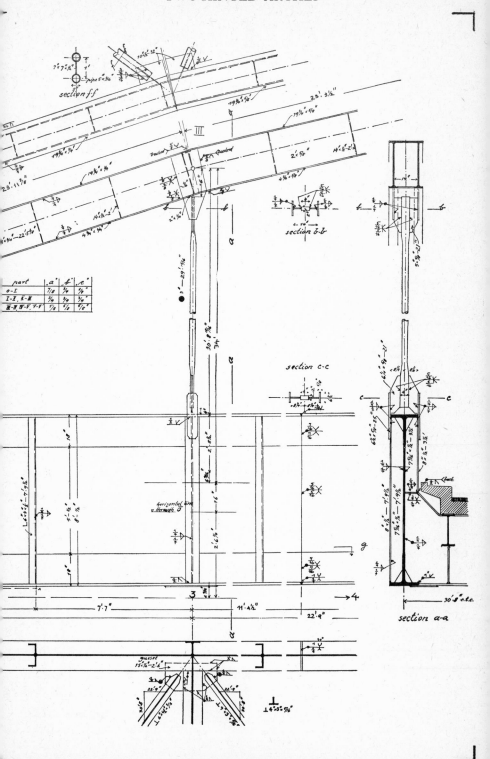

Figure 9 (Concluded)

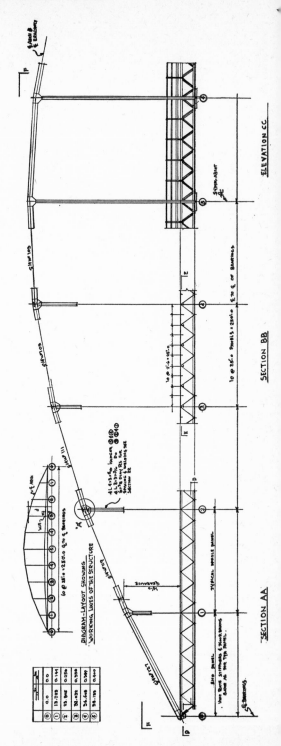

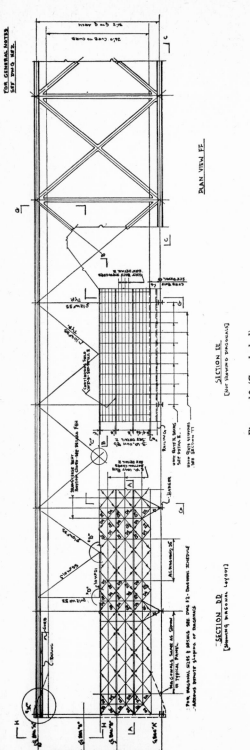

SECTION EE
[Not Showing Diagonals]

SECTION DD
[Showing Diagonal Layout]

PLAN VIEW FE

Figure 10 (Concluded)

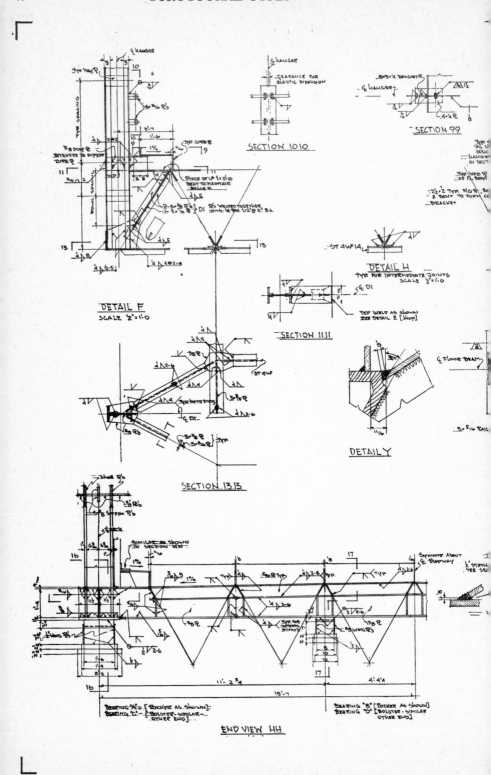

Figure 11

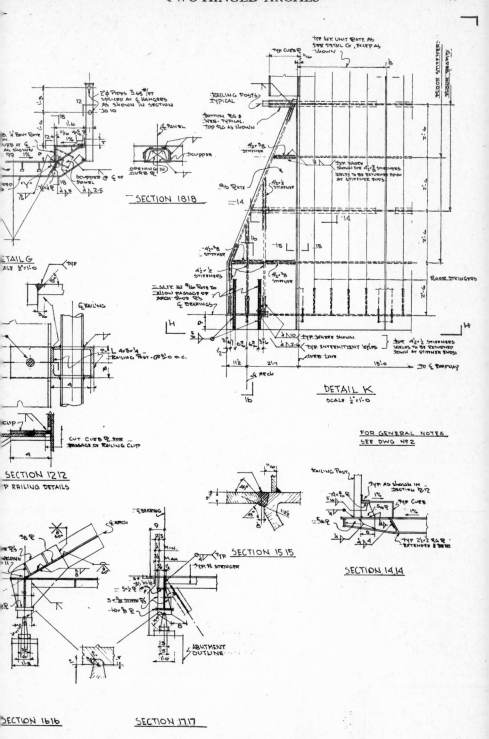

Figure 11 (Concluded)

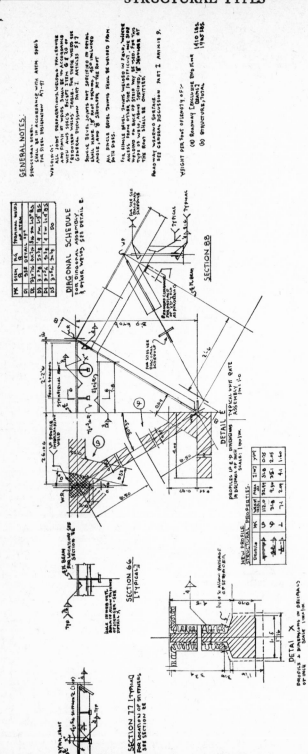

Figure 12

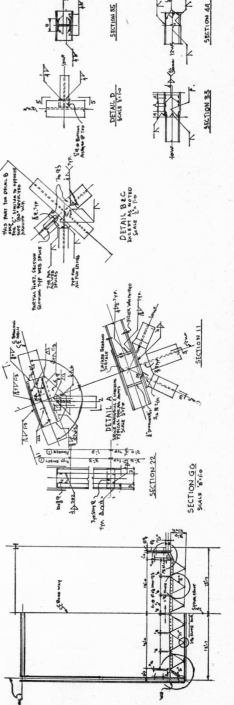

Figure 12 (Concluded)

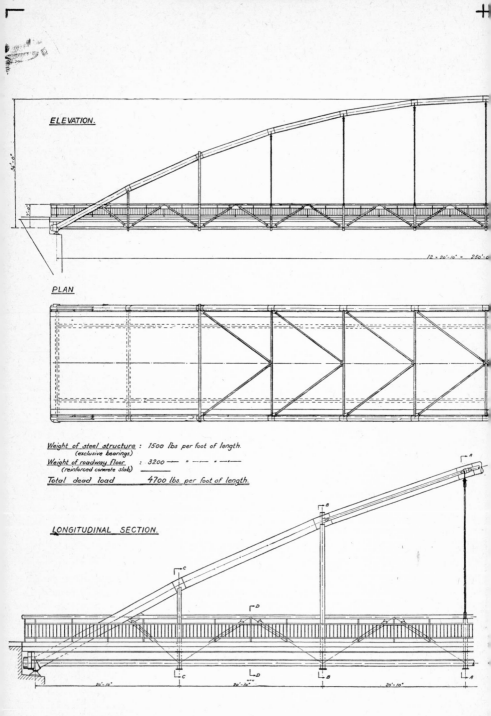

ELEVATION.

34'-0"

PLAN

12 × 20'-10" = 250'-0"

Weight of steel structure : 1500 lbs per foot of length.
    (exclusive bearings)
Weight of roadway floor   : 3200   "   "   "   "   "
    (reinforced concrete slab)
Total dead load   4700 lbs per foot of length.

LONGITUDINAL SECTION.

20'-10"   20'-10"   20'-10"

Figure 13

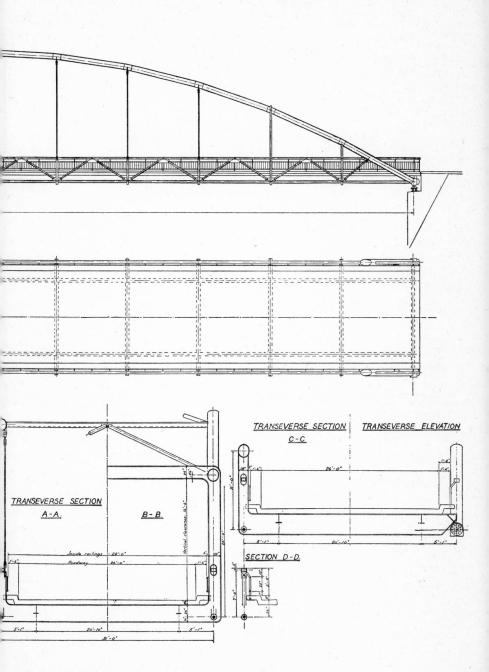

TRANSEVERSE SECTION
C-C

TRANSEVERSE ELEVATION

TRANSEVERSE SECTION
A-A.

B-B

SECTION D-D.

Figure 13 (Concluded)

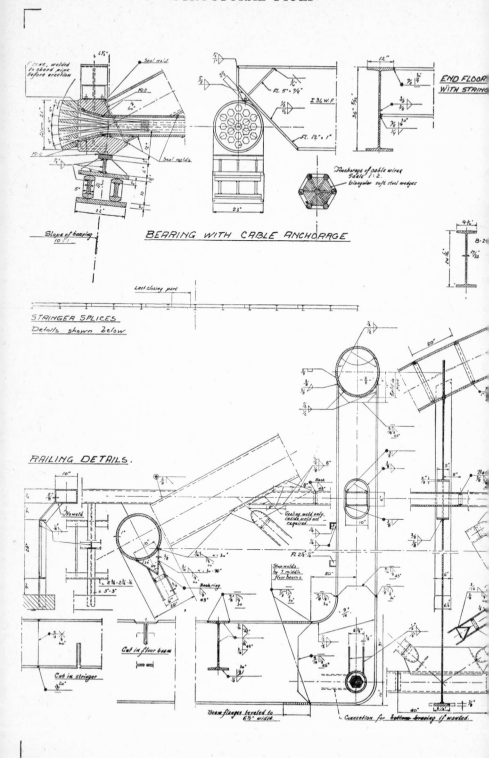

BEARING WITH CABLE ANCHORAGE

STRINGER SPLICES
Details shown below

RAILING DETAILS.

Figure 14

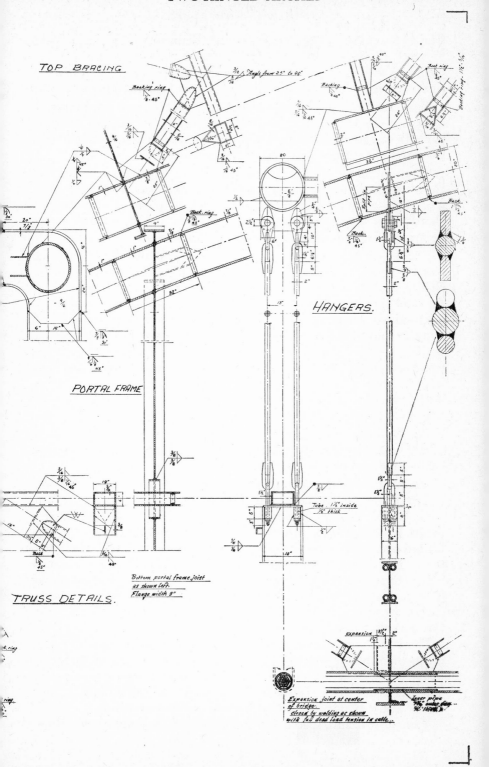

Figure 14 (Concluded)

The arch section is a large pipe (outside diameter = 20 in., thickness = 1 in.), seamless or welded, which gives the ideal section for low steel weight as well as for maintenance. The arch pipes are to be sealed air-tight, through which operation they are secured against inner corrosion.

"For each arch, a twistless cable is used as the main tension tie. It consists of 19 x 7 = 133 wires, with diameter =⅜ in. and breaking strength of about 150,000 lb. per sq. in. In this way, an unspliced tension section (100 per cent effective) is obtained.

"The stiffening girder [truss] consists of pipes and rectangular closed sections, giving ideal compression members, closed air-tight, whereby a minimum of maintenance area is obtained. The bottom chord pipe encloses and protects the tie cable, and after erection may be press filled with a suitable asphalt composition."

The bridge is divided into 12 equal panels. At the first and second panel points at each end, the vertical hangers are I shape members rigidly attached to the floorbeams. The other interior hangers have the same type of rigid members up to the rectangular top chord of the longitudinal stiffening truss. From this point up to the arch, these hangers consist of two rounds each 2 in. in diameter. The top lateral bracing begins at the second panel point and is 8 panels long. It has transverse struts that are 8 in. by 5 in. rectangular sections and 6-in. pipe for diagonals. The reinforced concrete floor acts as the bottom lateral bracing. At each field splice of the main arch pipe, inner rings are used as backing material for the welds.

An elevation, a longitudinal section, and three transverse sections of this bridge are given in Figure 13 and the details of the connections, splices, and end bearing are shown in Figure 14.

Mr. Arild states that any inquiries concerning patents should be sent to him or the Norwegian Patent Bureau.

T. N. W. Akroyd, Ormskirk, Lancashire, England, presented a design which could be described either as a bowstring type or a two-hinged arch with stiffening girder acting as the tie. His description was: "The bridge, being of the bowstring type, is of good appearance and is in simple taste. Without any added ornaments it depends for its beauty on the form of its arch and stiffener girder. All superfluous parts have been cut out and the structure does its job with economy, ease and efficiency."

The stiffening girder is supported every 25 ft. by hanger rods, 2¾ in. in diameter. It is composed of a 24 x ¾ web welded to 24 x 6 flange tees ("New Welding Tee") and has a total depth of 3 ft.-2 in. The arch is of I shape also, having either a 34 x ⅞ web welded to 27 x 7 tees or a 36 x ¾ web welded to 24 x 6 tees. The rise is 30 ft.

Transverse beams, spaced at 6 ft.-3 in. centers, frame into the stiffening girders and support the roadway so that no stringers are required. These cross beams are similar to the lateral struts between the arch ribs. They are "Broad Flange Beams castellated, i.e. cut and rewelded in the web (British Patent Rights No. 498281)." The lateral struts at panel points two to eight, inclusive, constitute the entire web system for the arch bracing—there are no diagonal members. The roadway is made up of 9 x 2 tees, placed together with the webs upward and having the space between the webs filled with concrete. This roadway construction eliminates the need of additional lower lateral bracing. The details of the floor are shown in Figures 79 and 80 in Chapter III where it is discussed more fully. Some details of the stiffening girder and the splices of the arch rib are included in these figures. Figure 15 shows the elevations and sections of the arch rib and the connections between the arch rib and the lateral struts.

Mr. Akroyd in discussing his design said:

"Apart from the fact that the tee sections and webs are curved, the arch is as simple as the stiffener girder. It is of deeper section than the stiffener girder, which draws attention to its position as the primary member. . . .

"The bowstring girder and arch are always beautiful and economic in material because of the arch member which is both light and strong. The wind bracing of the arch has been reduced to a minimum to give a clear, neat appearance and extra stiffness has, as mentioned, been given to the flooring.

"The more simple the details of the bridge, the less the chances of undetected corrosion. The weak spots of a steel bridge are always at the joints of members, it is here that corrosion more easily takes place. For these two reasons special attention should always be given to the design of joints, this has been carried out and the simplest types evolved.

"It is felt that undetected corrosion is impossible with the detailing shown. The life of the bridge should be long; it is difficult to estimate a number of years, but it will certainly not be less than 80 years."

Two-Hinged Arches
B. With Ties

Of the designs included in this group, many have trussed arch ribs, some have ribs with solid webs, and one has a Vierendeel type of arch rib. In these bridges, the ties are designed to take only the longitudinal component of the arch thrust and do not serve as stiffening members for the arch; even so, the differences in the ties of these bridges is marked—for example, one design uses a steel floor plate to serve also as the tie and another uses the continuous stringers as the tie.

E. R. Bretscher and J. W. Briscoe, both of Urbana, Illinois, commented on their design as follows:

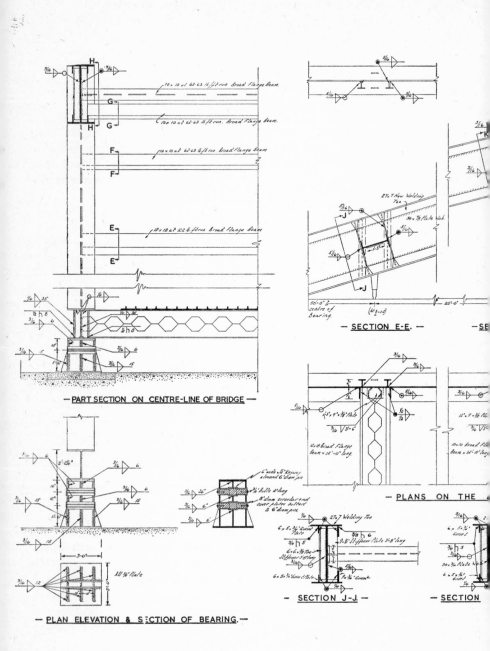

— PART SECTION ON CENTRE-LINE OF BRIDGE —

— PLAN ELEVATION & SECTION OF BEARING. —

— SECTION E-E. —

— PLANS ON THE

— SECTION J-J —

— SECTION

Figure 15

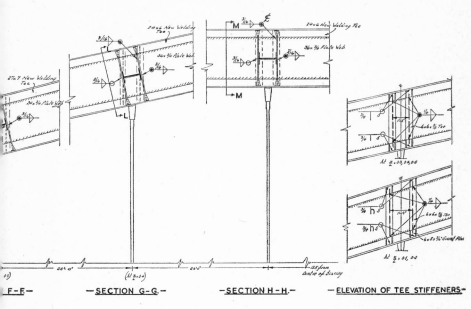

| —F-F— | —SECTION G-G.— | —SECTION H-H.— | —ELEVATION OF TEE STIFFENERS— |

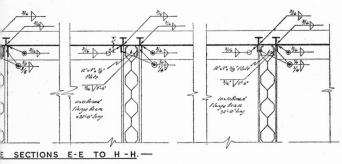

— SECTIONS E-E TO H-H. —

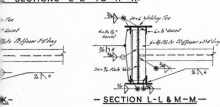

— SECTION L-L & M—M.—

Figure 15 (Concluded)

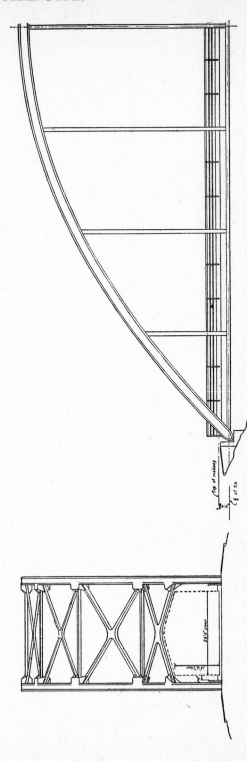

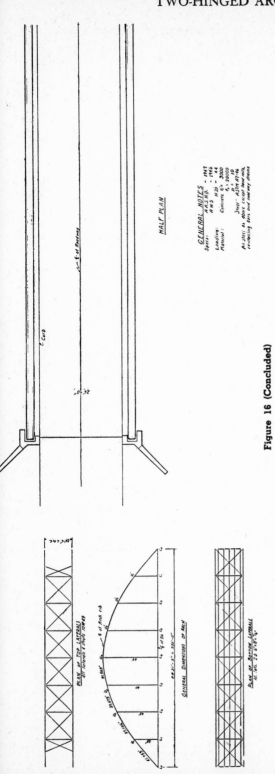

Figure 16 (Concluded)

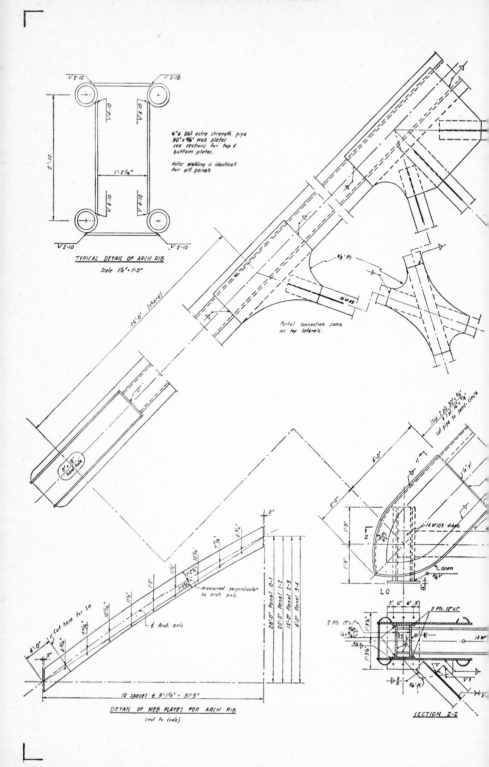

TYPICAL DETAIL OF ARCH RIB
Scale 1½" = 1'-0"

6"∅ Dbl. extra strength pipe
30" x 96" web plates
see sections for top &
bottom plates.

Note: Welding is identical
for all panels.

Portal connection same
as top laterals.

DETAIL OF WEB PLATES FOR ARCH RIB
(not to scale)

SECTION 2-2

Figure 17

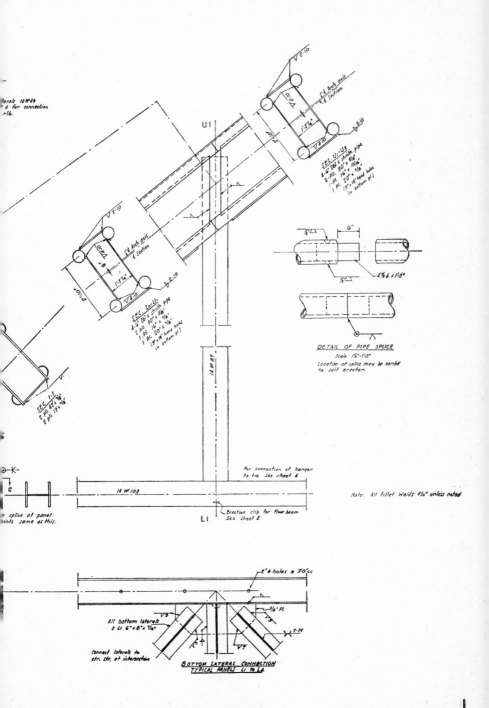

DETAIL OF PIPE SPLICE
Scale 1½"=1'-0"
Location of splice may be varied
to suit erection.

Figure 17 (Concluded)

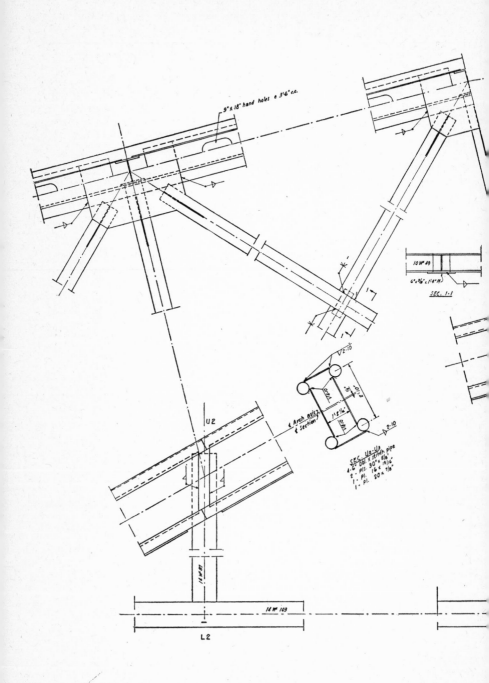

Figure 18

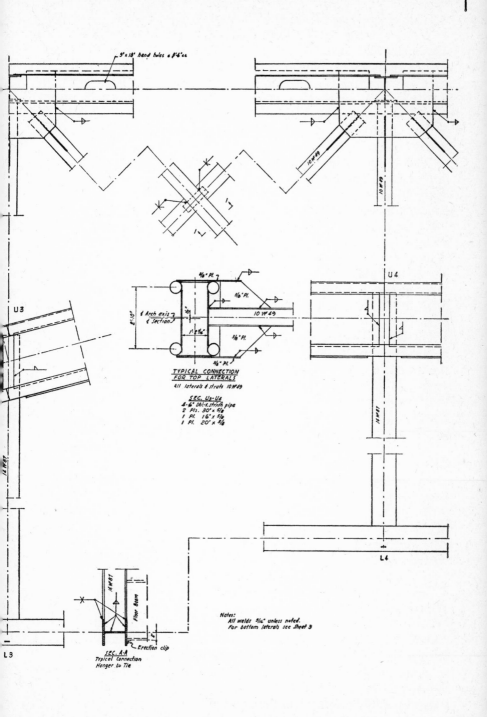

Figure 18 (Concluded)

"This design may be called a 'Welded Bridge of Today', as well as a 'Welded Bridge of the Future'. The design is based entirely on shapes that are available today, and the connections are all simple welded connections. However, this is not simply a riveted bridge revised for welding. The arch rib could not be fabricated by riveting. It is suitable only for welded construction. Except for the arch rib the main carrying members, the tie and hangers, are in tension. With welded construction, there is no loss of section in these members due to rivet holes.

"The outline of the structure clearly expresses its function as a two-hinged arch. The parabolic arch rib, combined with the simple lines of the hangers and the horizontal lines of the railing and tie give the structure an appearance of quiet strength."

Figure 16 shows that the arch is divided into eight panels and has a rise of 64 ft. Each arch rib utilizes four double strength pipes (6 in. in diameter), two 30 x ⅝ web plates, one top plate (16 in. wide), and one bottom plate (20 in. in width). Access to the inside of this box-shape section is possible through the 9-in. by 18-in. hand holes which occur in the bottom plate. The top and bottom plates vary in thickness from ⅞ in. for the end panel to ⅝ in. at the center.

The lateral bracing between the two arch ribs is composed entirely of the same rolled shape—10 WF 49. This includes the members of the portal, the transverse struts, and the diagonals. Each rib is tied with a 14 WF 103 section. The hangers are 14 WF 103 sections. For the bottom lateral bracing system, the diagonal members consist of 2 angles, 6 x 8 x ⁷⁄₁₆, and the floorbeams act as the struts. Connections and details of the bracing, arch rib, and tie are part of Figures 17 and 18. The reinforced concrete slab and the floor system is discussed in Chapter III.

Messrs. Bretscher and Briscoe discussed erection, maintenance, and probable life:

"Joints on the arch rib are made by means of steel plugs in the ends of the pipes. The sections are slipped over plugs, in the pipe in the adjoining panel, just like an erector set. The hangers fit inside the section and complete the splice. Welding of the pipe need not be done immediately, since the plugs will keep the section in line.

"The floorbeam is positioned and held in place for welding by means of Saxe welded connection units. Thus erection is comparatively simple.

"All steel is easily accessible for painting. The inside of the six-inch pipe in the rib section which could not be painted in the field is plugged at each end, and thus sealed against corrosion.

"Since the design is based on the most conservative interpretation of the A.A.S.H.O. Specifications, we may expect a life span at least equal to, and possibly greater than the average."

J. T. Percy, Troy, New York, chose for his design the "Crescent Truss" shown in Figure 19. It is a two-hinged arch with trussed arch ribs. It is divided into nine panels and has a maximum height (from tie to the top of the truss) at mid-span of 40 ft.

The members of the truss, the members of both the top and bottom lateral bracing systems, and the tie beam are all rolled sections. The top laterals are 10 WF 33 as shown in Figure 21, the diagonals in the bottom bracing are 12 WF 65, the tie beam is a 14 WF 211, and all members of the truss are 14 WF of various sizes. About the latter, he said:

"All members in the trusses are 14 WF sections. The advantage of using this section was that so many sizes were available from which to choose, that a weight saving was obtained, because of the relatively small excess in allowable strengths.

"By using all 14 WF sections the butt welding of adjoining members was made easier. In most cases it would be unnecessary for extra precautions in welding for butting ends are of same thickness.

"The use of curved joint connections between chord and web members may be questionable because of the increased fabricating costs. However, it is the belief of the author that they are justifiable on aesthetic grounds and on their ability to reduce stress concentrations. If fabricating cost were too high the curved fillets can be readily omitted."

A typical connection of the truss members is shown in Figure 20. Each hanger is made of four—1⅛-in. bridge cables. The filled I-Beam-Lok floor and the continuous stringers are discussed in Chapter III.

Robert Forster, Cleveland, Ohio, gave the following general description of his bridge:

"The bridge consists of two tied arches spaced 31 ft. apart on centers. Each arch is a truss whose top and bottom chord panel points lie on parabolic curves [see Figure 22] having vertices 20 ft.-4 in. and 37 ft.-6 in. high respectively. Six stringers, spaced 6.2 ft. apart, are designed as fully continuous members to perform two functions; first, to carry and transfer the weight of the reinforced concrete roadway and live load to the supporting floorbeams; and second, to perform as ties for restraint of horizontal translation of the ends of each arch truss. The restraining tensile force in the stringers acting as ties are transferred to two horizontal end trusses in the plane of the stringers at each end of the bridge. The horizontal end trusses are 12.4 ft. in depth and are proportioned to transmit the stringer forces to the ends of each arch.

"Floorbeams are distributed transversely under the continuous stringers at 20 ft-10 in. intervals. The end reactions of the floorbeams are transferred to suspenders which are attached to the panel points of the arches.

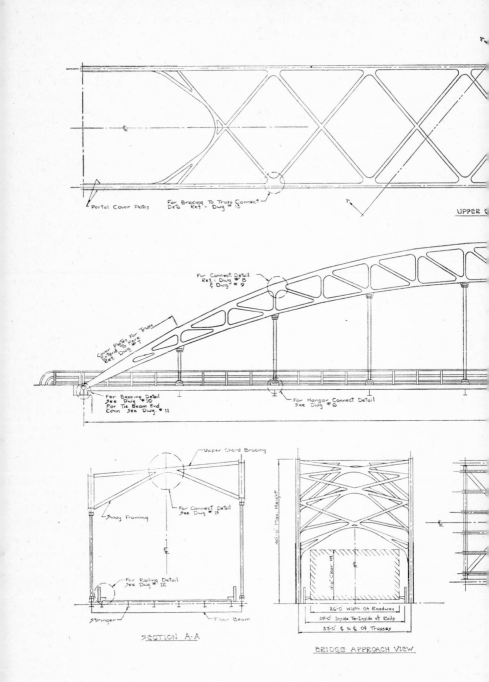

Portal Cover Plates

For Bracing To Truss Connect
Deto Ref' - Dwg # 13

UPPER C

For Connect Detail
Ref : Dwg # 8
& Dwg # 9

Cover Plates For Truss
Extend To Her
Ref : Dwg # 7

For Bearing Detail
See Dwg # 10
For Tie Beam End
Conn See Dwg # 11

For Hanger Connect Detail
See Dwg # 6

Upper Chord Bracing

For Connect Detail
See Dwg # 15

Sway Framing

For Railing Detail
See Dwg # 12

Stringer

Floor Beam

SECTION A-A

40'-0 Max Height

16'-0 Clear Ht

26'-0 Width Of Roadway

24'-0 Inside To-Inside of Rails

33'-0 ℄ to ℄ Of Trusses

BRIDGE APPROACH VIEW

Figure 19

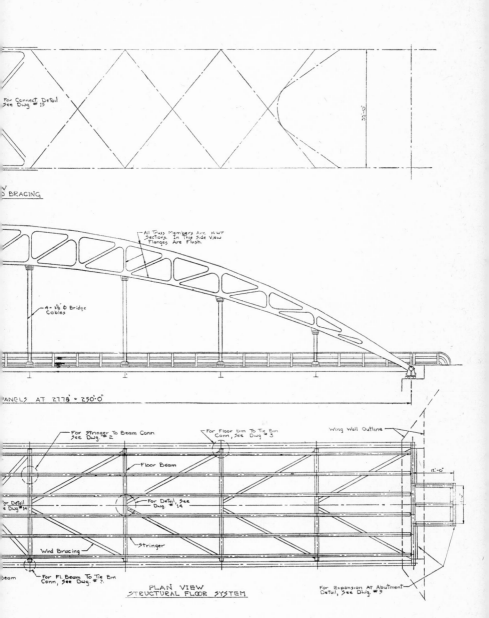

For Connect Detail
See Dwg # 15

25'-0"

BRACING

All Truss Members Are WWF
Sections. In This Side View
Flanges Are Flush.

4 - 1⅛" Ø Bridge
Cables

PANELS AT 27.78' = 250'-0"

For Stringer To Beam Conn.
See Dwg. # 2

For Floor Bm To Tie Bm
Conn, See Dwg # 3

Wing Wall Outline

Floor Beam

12'-0"

For Detail
See Dwg #14

For Detail, See
Dwg. # 14

Wind Bracing

Stringer

Beam

For Fl Beam To Tie Bm
Conn, See Dwg. # 3

PLAN VIEW
STRUCTURAL FLOOR SYSTEM

For Expansion At Abutment
Detail, See Dwg. # 5

Figure 19 (Concluded)

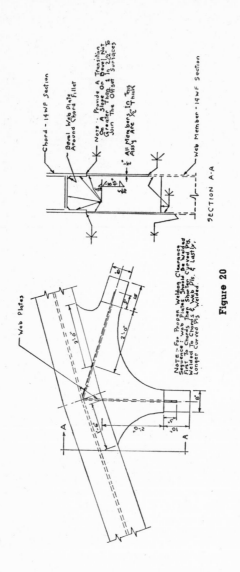

Figure 20

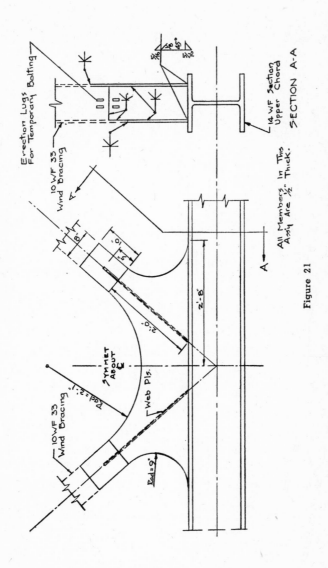

Figure 21

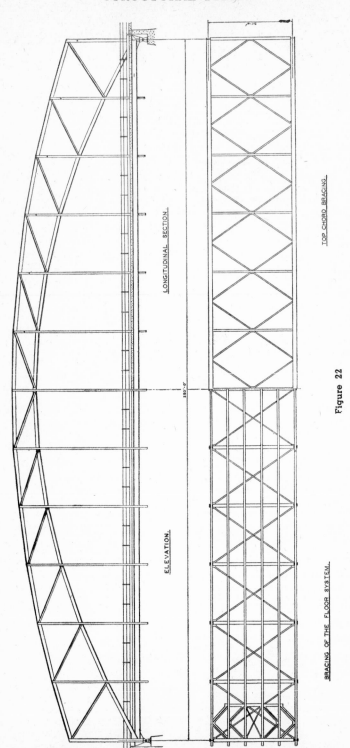

LONGITUDINAL SECTION.

TOP CHORD BRACING.

ELEVATION.

BRACING OF THE FLOOR SYSTEM.

Figure 22

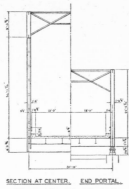

SECTION AT CENTER.   END PORTAL.

Figure 22 (Concluded)

"Wind bracing is provided in the plane of the top chords of the main trusses and in the plane of the bottom chords of the stringers to transfer lateral forces into the bridge bearings. In every transverse plane through the panel points of the arches, portals of sufficient stiffness are placed to transmit wind loads from the bottom chords to the top chord wind bracing and to support the bottom chord against lateral buckling.

"The cross section of all structural members subjected to large forces was chosen of such form as to facilitate the use of a butt weld which is the most effective connection between two steel units. Consequently, the T section was used wherever practicable, since it lends itself best to butt welding."

Mr. Forster developed special T sections with web thicknesses equal to those of the flanges. These new shapes are discussed, and their dimensions are given, in Chapter IV.

The sizes and end connections of the members of the arch truss are given in Figure 23. The flanges are tees, the diagonals are two angles, and the verticals are rolled WF sections. The hangers of this design are composed of four 3½ x 2½ x ⁵⁄₁₆ angles. Details of the horizontal end trusses and details of the bracing are shown in Figure 67 of Chapter III where the floor system is discussed. Flat plates are used in the design of the horizontal end trusses.

K. H. Seegers, Gustavsburg, Germany, described the type of bridge he designed in the following words:

"The proposed type is a kind of tied arch. The roadway construction has the function of the tie. Its stiffness is taken into account. The arch is of hollow-box-type. Its interior is accessible. The suspenders are ropes."

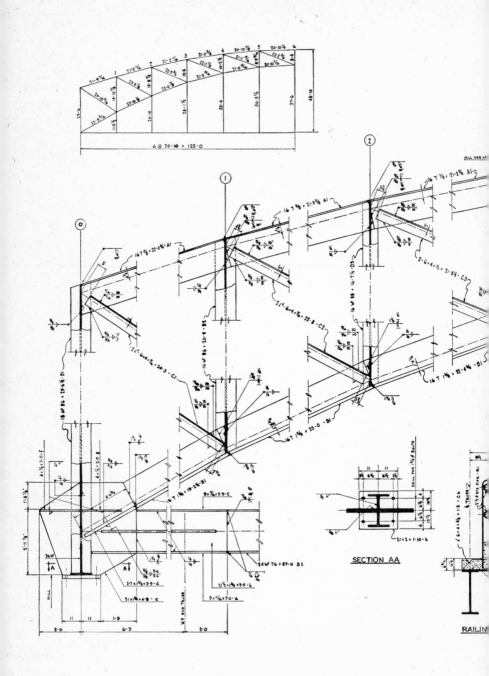

Figure 23

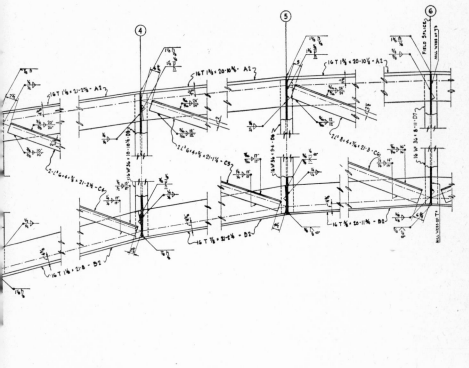

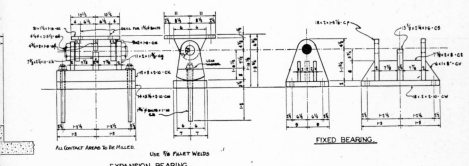

EXPANSION BEARING.

FIXED BEARING.

DETAIL.

Figure 23 (Concluded)

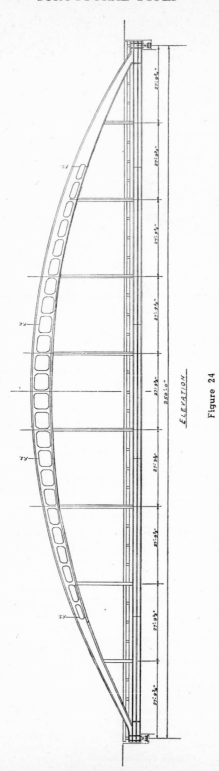

ELEVATION

Figure 24

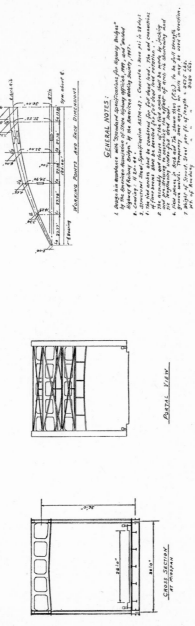

Figure 24 (Concluded)

The roadway is supported by rope hangers (two—1¼ in. in diameter) at 20 ft.-10 in. centers. The arch ribs are box sections approximately 4 feet deep and 1 ft.-9 in. wide, made up of two flange plates and two web plates. The rise of the arch is about 30 ft. at the center. The two ribs are braced together with a stiff box-shape portal member at the second panel point from each end. Between these portals, the diagonals and struts of the lateral bracing system are rolled beams.

The steel roadway serves the purpose of the floor slab, the bottom lateral bracing, and the tie for the arch. The horizontal plate with stiffeners in both directions is to be fabricated in long units. These units will be placed on two longitudinal girders and on cross girders and welded to them. The plate is the top flange for all of the floor system members whether they are longitudinal or transverse members. Thus, the longitudinal thrust of the arch ribs is distributed over the entire floor system structure. For details of the floor system see Figure 76 page 178.

Zusse Levinton, New York, New York, presented a tied arch bridge of novel design that uses open-web girders (Vierendeel trusses) of variable depth as the arch ribs. In describing these main supporting members, he said:

"The arch ribs are crescent shaped, with a parabolic axis rising 36 ft. above the centerline of the tie. The crescent rib is of open rigid-frame construction, except the ends, or horns of the crescent, which are of solid-webbed box construction. The crescent has a uniform taper from 8-ft. depth at the center of the span to 2-ft. depth at the ends.

"For the construction of the crescent rigid frame, new rolled sections are proposed. These sections are 'Double Tees', consisting of a flange 24 in. wide, 1½ in. thick and two webs 12 in. by ¾ in. These sections are used for the top and bottom chords of the crescent frame. For the vertical members of the frame, 14-in. wide flange beams are used, with special fillet plates at the corners, in the planes of the two webs of the double-tee chord members.

*   *   *

"For the tie member of the arch, a new rolled 'E' section is proposed, 36 in. deep, with 6-in. flanges, web and flanges ½ in. thick. The two 'E' sections of the tie are 12½ in. back to back and are connected by tie plates 3 ft. apart on their top and bottom flanges."

An elevation, a cross section, and a portal view of this bridge are included in Figure 24. Mr. Levinton stated: "The main feature of this design is the simplicity and elegance of the general appearance of the bridge, as well as simplicity and compactness of its details." For information regarding patent rights of this design contact the author.

Two-Hinged Arches
C. Without Ties

The following designs have the hinges at both ends fixed against longitudinal movement—the abutments take both the longitudinal and vertical thrusts from the arch ribs.

Ernst Amstutz, Zurich, Switzerland, chose a two-hinged arch bridge of ten panels with a rather slender appearance (see Figure 25). The rise of the arch is 25 ft. Each of the two ribs is a cylinder, ½ in. thick and 3 ft. in diameter except for the end panels. The cylinders are 2 ft. in diameter at the abutments and increase uniformly in diameter within the end panels to the 3 ft. diameter. The hinges at the abutments are 3 ft-4 in. above the roadway surface. The lateral bracing for the arch cylinders consists of large transverse struts spaced at 50 ft. intervals. These struts are tubes which vary in diameter (See Figure 26). Their diameter is 30 in. at the intersection with the rib and 12 in. for the middle 10 ft. Their thickness is ⁵⁄₁₆ in.

The arch is stiffened by a single stiffening girder located beneath the center of the roadway. This stiffening girder is of semi-circular shape, having a 5-ft. radius. The thickness of the plate is ⁷⁄₁₆ in. or ⅜ in. depending on its longitudinal location. A folded deck plate serves as the top flange of the stiffening girder. The concrete filled deck plate is made from a ⅜-in. plate which has been folded into trapezoidal corrugations having a 4-in. depth. This detail is given in Figure 27.

The hangers are two—1½-in. rounds which form a loop to support the ends of the floorbeams which cantilever out from the single stiffening girder. The box-shape curbs are actually structural members acting integrally with the folded deck plate and the main semi-circular girder to form a longitudinal unit. Running transverse to the roadway, one-inch round bars both above and below the folded deck plate are spaced at 6-in. centers. Being welded to the deck plate, these bars become transverse trusses 5 in. deep capable of distributing wheel loads transversely between the structural curbs and the main girder in the center.

As Mr. Amstutz said, this design could be transformed into a tied arch with only little changes. Also he remarked that the single longitudinal girder not only reduced cost but that, being located in the center, the smaller curbs dominate the side view to improve the slender appearance. He called attention to the advantages of the torsional stiffness of the main girder and the curbs, the resistance to buckling of the cylindrical members, and the elimination of bottor lateral bracing.

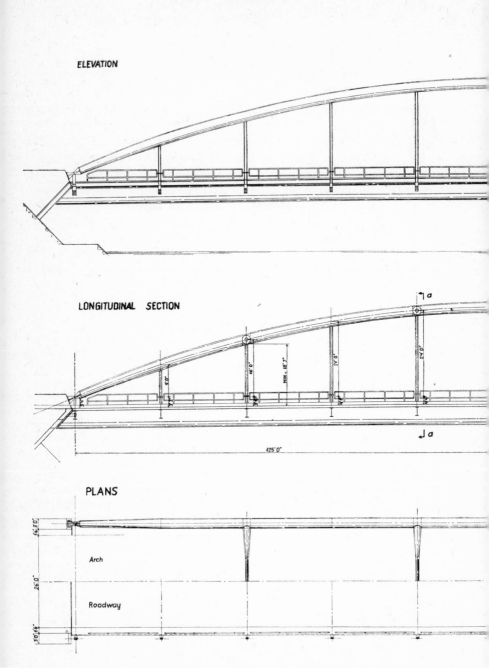

ELEVATION

LONGITUDINAL SECTION

PLANS

Arch

Roadway

Figure 25

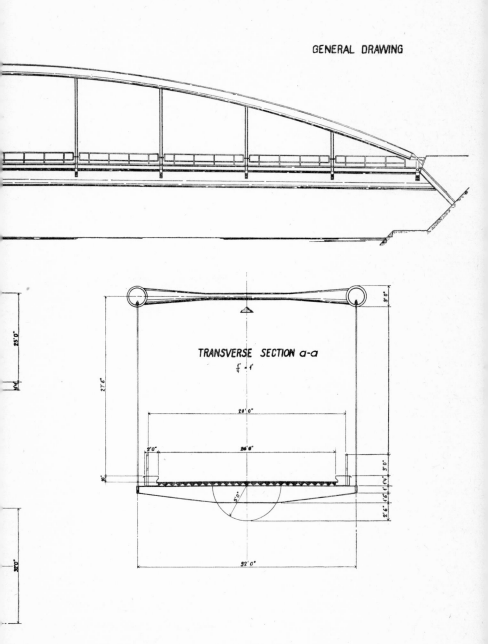

Figure 25 (Concluded)

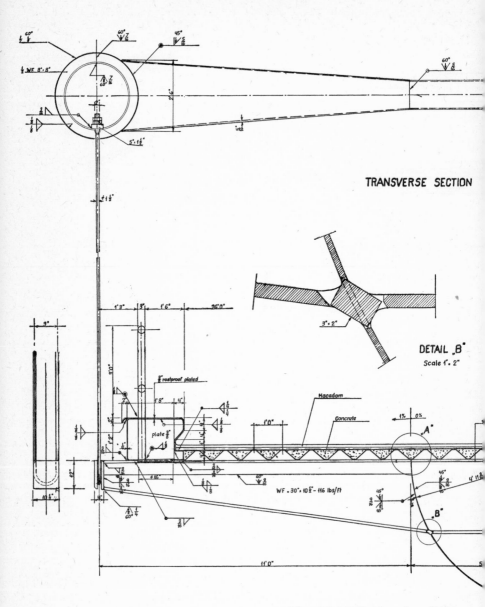

TRANSVERSE SECTION

DETAIL "B"
Scale 1" = 2"

weight per foot of length of the roadway = 1080 lbs.

weight per foot of length of the steel structure 1840 lbs.

Figure 26

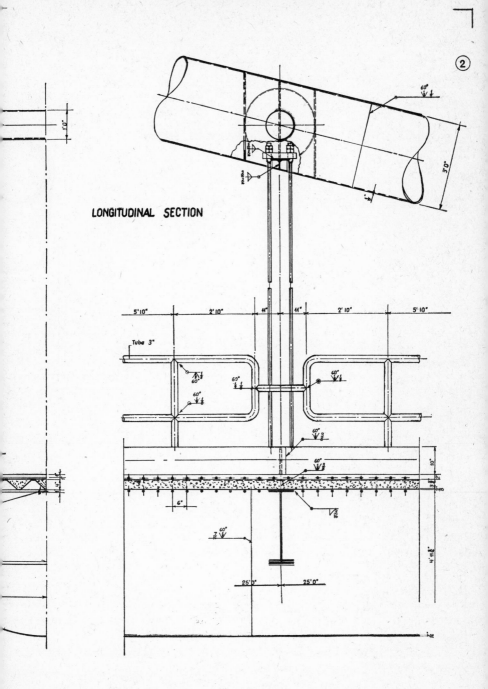

LONGITUDINAL SECTION

Figure 26 (Concluded)

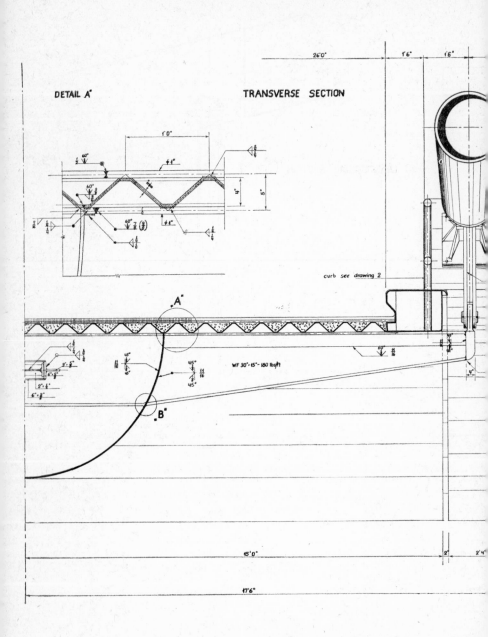

Figure 27

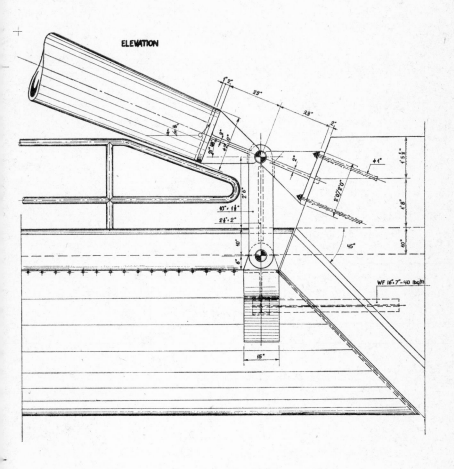

ELEVATION

Figure 27 (Concluded)

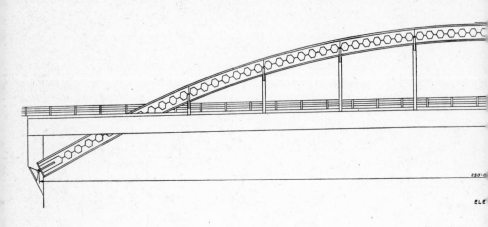

ELE

250'-0

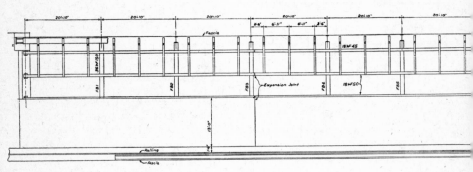

PART PLAN
Showing Roadway and Framing

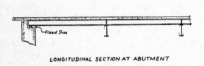

LONGITUDINAL SECTION AT ABUTMENT

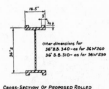

CROSS-SECTION OF PROPOSED ROLLED
"BULB BEAMS"
36 B.B. 340 and 36 B.B. 310

TYPICAL ARCH DETAIL

Figure 28

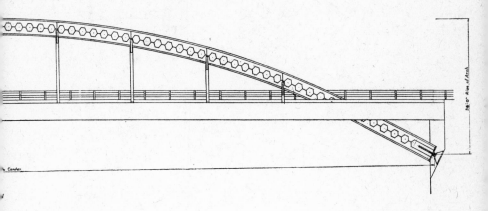

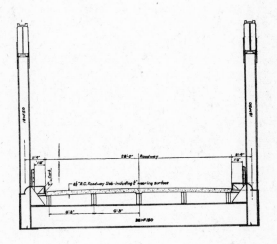

CROSS SECTION

Weight of Roadway .... 2,120 lbs/lin. ft.
Weight of Steel Structure .... 1,580 lbs/lin. ft.

Figure 28 (Concluded)

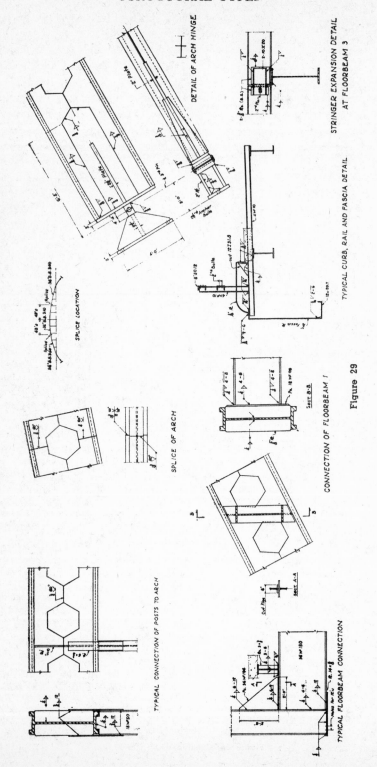

Figure 29

H. H. Bleich, New York, New York, gave this description of his bridge:

"The proposed bridge is a two-hinged arch without lateral bracing, having a concrete roadway slab carried on stringers and floorbeams suspended from the arch.

"The essential features of the bridge are the choice of section and the design method for the arch. In order to avoid lateral bracing, which is both unsightly and costly, it is necessary to use a section of as large a lateral radius of gyration as possible. The section should be such that as much of the material as possible is concentrated in the corners of the arch cross section. To obtain such a section with a minimum of labor, a new rolled section, called 'Bulb Beam', is proposed. The shape of the proposed rolled section is a wide flange beam with added 'bulbs', which place the material just where it does the most good. The bulbs increase the lateral radius of gyration by about 30 per cent.

"As the shear stresses in the web of the arch are low, the 36-in. deep bulb beams are cut horizontally and welded together forming a 48-in. deep section with hexagonal holes in the web of the arch.

"The compression chords of the arch section were designed as columns on elastic supports as required by AASHO Specification 3.6.70, but the first paragraph of this same specification requiring a certain strength of the vertical members and floorbeam connections was disregarded as being unnecessarily severe. Instead, the vertical members and floorbeam connections were analyzed as outlined in the appendix of this report. [This report is not included here].

"To avoid action of the floor system as tie of the arch, provision for expansion of the concrete deck slab and of the stringers was made at the quarter points of the span. The deck slab and stringers form an effective bracing system in spite of these expansion joints; this was achieved by providing fixed shoes where the stringers rest on the abutments. For horizontal loads the end portions of the roadway slab and the stringers form cantilever beams of about 60-foot span, and the center portion of the slab acts as suspended span.

"The steel railing, bent steel plates forming the curbs, and fascia plates are supported by transverse 4-in. H beams carried from the stringers.

"The proposed structure should be cheap in first cost, as well as in maintenance, because it consists of a very small number of members and does not require expensive fabrication.

"The probable life of the structure will be equal, or possibly longer, than that of a conventional riveted structure.

"Due to the omission of lateral bracing, the appearance of the bridge is considerably better than the appearance of the conventional type of arch with bracing."

A plan, an elevation, and a cross section of this bridge are shown in Figure 28, and the structural details are shown in Figure 29.

Three-Hinged Arches

Most of the three-hinged arches were tied, and about fifty per cent of them had stiffening girders. For a majority of the designs, the arches were rectangular in cross section; however, one design had tubular arch ribs, and for another, the arch ribs were lune shaped trusses.

A. A. Brielmaier and J. A. DeLong, both of St. Louis, Missouri, said the following about the general features and appearance of their bridge:

"It is a through type, three-hinged tied arch with stiffening girder. The roadway consists of open steel grating with sills on continuous steel stringers spaced at 4 ft-10 in., which rest on the transverse floorbeams spaced at 25 ft-0 in.

"The floorbeams frame into the stiffening girders, which are 32 ft.-0 in. apart. Four hangers, at intervals of 50 ft-0 in., connect each stiffening girder to the arch above.

"Each arch has a hinge at the crown and also at each end of the span. The lower hinges are attached to the top flange of the stiffening girder. Lateral wind forces against the arches themselves are transferred by a system of diagonals to the ends of the arches where, by means of portal framing, they are brought down to the lower hinges and thence to the bridge bearings. Lateral wind forces against traffic and against the girders and floor system are transferred to the bridge bearings by a lower lateral bracing system consisting of the floorbeams and double diagonals.

"The structure presents a clear, clean appearance. When it is viewed from the side, the lines of the stiffening girder and of the railing together form a pleasing, horizontal pattern. Above is the smooth sweep of the arch, uncluttered by any projecting details. Between the horizontal lines of the girder and the smooth curve of the arch, there are only the four vertical lines of the hangers, wide enough to be apparent, but narrow enough to express subordination to the heavier members which they connect.

"The depth of the stiffening girder completely conceals the details of the floor framing.

"The motorist using the bridge sees, in addition to the arch and the hangers, the members of the top bracing system between the arches. The bracing members, however, fit in well with the arches since they are completely enclosed with clear lines and have no projections, openings or distracting details. To the motorist, the bridge offers an essentially unobstructed side view approaching that from a deck bridge. The wide spacing of the hangers, although it may have slightly in-

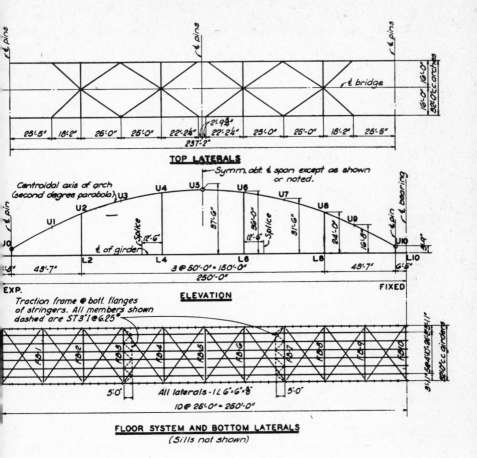

TOP LATERALS

ELEVATION

FLOOR SYSTEM AND BOTTOM LATERALS
(Sills not shown)

HALF SECTION A-A
(Showing interior floorbeams FB-1 to FB-9, incl.)

Figure 30

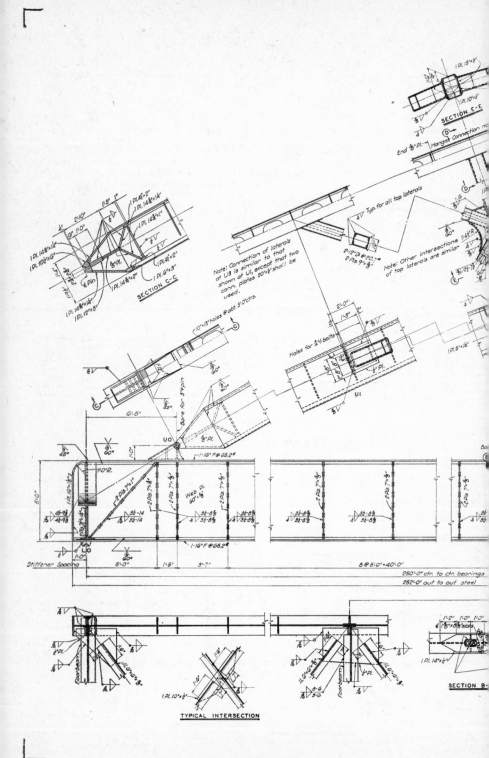

TYPICAL INTERSECTION

SECTION B-

Figure 31

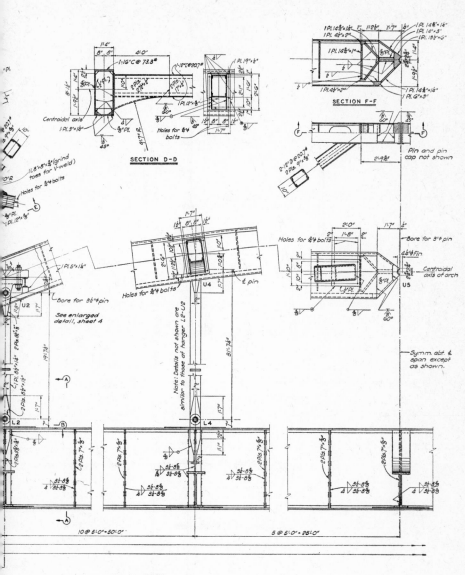

Figure 31 (Concluded)

NOTES
For details of special sections, see sheet 4.
For details of girder splice, see sheet 4.
For Section A-A, see sheet 2.

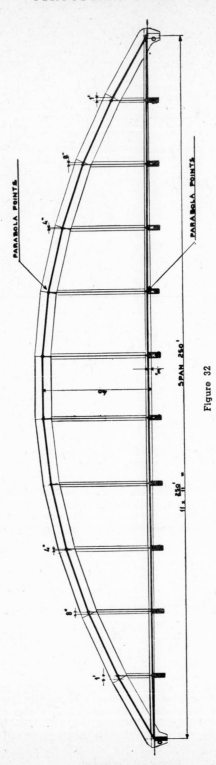

Figure 32

creased the weight of the bridge, is of the greatest value in enhancing the appearance.

"It is difficult to imagine a truss on this span, of either the through or deck type, which can compete with the pleasing effect of this arch with stiffening girder and widely spaced hangers."

As shown in Figure 30, the center hinge of the arch is 37 ft-6 in. above the center line of the girder at the middle of the span. The centroidal axis of the arch is a second degree parabola.

Figure 31 shows the details of the members and their connections. The tie girder is 5 ft-6 in. deep, composed of special tees as flanges and a 60-in. by ⅝-in. web plate. The arch rib is a rectangular section 1 ft.-4 in. wide and 3 ft-1½ in. deep. The top is a special channel and the webs and bottom are plates. A small plate, 3 in. by 1¼ in., is welded inside each bottom corner. The upper lateral bracing system has box members made of two channels and two plates. The hangers are 8½ by 1¼ plates which are pin-connected to the stiffening girder and to the arch rib.

In this design, the tie is also a stiffening girder, but special attachments are used between the stringers and floorbeams to prevent the stringers from participating in the tie-action for the arch. These attachments are shown and discussed in Chapter III.

A. A. Mulder, Utrecht, The Netherlands, designed a tied, three-hinged arch bridge (See Figure 32). The arch ribs are rectangular in shape, 3 ft. wide and 6 ft. deep. They are braced laterally by rectangular struts, 1 ft.-6 in. wide and 2 ft.-10 in. deep, located just below the arch ribs at eight of the ten interior panel points. The span is divided into eleven panels; however, there are no lateral struts at the first interior panel points (see Figure 33). The hangers are the same section as the lateral struts. The floorbeams are also box-shaped, 1 ft.-6 in. wide and 4 ft.-6 in. deep. Each hanger is connected to the arch rib, the lateral strut, and the floorbeam by a rigid connection so that these members form a large rectangular rigid frame at the panel points as shown in Figure 33.

All of the box sections are fabricated in a similar manner. As an example, a cross section of the arch rib is included in Figure 34 which is a detail drawing of the arch rib.

The floor plate, ½ in. thick, serves as the tie. At the ends, the floor plate is extended in width and welded directly to the arch ribs as shown in Figure 34. The floor plate is stiffened by channels (10 in. wide, 10 in. deep and ¼ in. thick) which are welded to the floor plate. This floor system is discussed in Chapter III.

As indicated above, Mr. Mulder used closed, rectangular sections exclusively. He wrote a lengthy discussion about the use of different

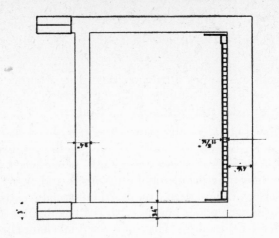

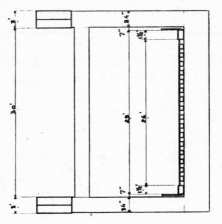

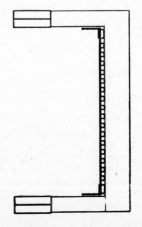

Figure 33

cross sections and brought out the fact that the "closed profile" is the only suitable section for compression, tension, bending, and torsion. He suggests that rectangular sections be built of two channels each of which is made from a flat plate rolled or pressed into shape because: "Rolling into the correct shape straightway from a block of steel meets with great difficulties of a technical nature in rolling, especially with large profiles." His remarks about the merits of the rectangular section are given in Chapter IV.

Because Mr. Mulder designed his bridge so that no erection bents are necessary, one of his remarks is as follows:

"If the middle hinge should be abandoned, the arch would turn out to be lighter, but then a temporary erection-support would be necessary, which would certainly be more expensive, while moreover the welding in the middle of the arch would have to be done overhead during the erection, which would not be permissible for such an important weld."

P. Gatzweiler and K. Kuhner, both of Heerlen, Holland, designed the bridge shown in Figure 35. It is a tied, three-hinged arch which is divided into fifteen panels and has a rise at mid-span of 32 ft.-10 in. The arch ribs and the ties are large tubes, approximately 4 ft. in diameter and ¾ in. thick. The hangers and top lateral members are also tubular in shape but much smaller in size.

The stringer spacing was about 4 ft.-1 in. "Bump plates" (buckle plates with a sag of about 7 in.) span the distance between the rolled stringers. These plates are filled and covered with crushed stone which is topped with a layer of asphaltic concrete.

Other Arched Structures

The arch bridges discussed here differ in at least one important respect from any of the designs of the previous classifications. These designs include fixed arches, an arch fixed at the ends but having intermediate hinges, and tied arches with hangers inclined (or radial) in the plane of the arch.

This classification does not include two designs which are arched in shape; one is a truncated A-frame, the other is a Vierendeel truss with an arched top chord. It seems appropriate that these two designs are discussed under the classification, "Miscellaneous Types."

J. R. Daymond and M. S. Zakrzewski, both of Durban, South Africa, designed an arch bridge which could be described as a fixed arch having two intermediate hinges; however, they preferred to describe it as follows: "The bridge is a two-hinged arch, the hinges being supported by inclined props which cantilever out from concrete abutments, the props also being splayed in plan." Because these

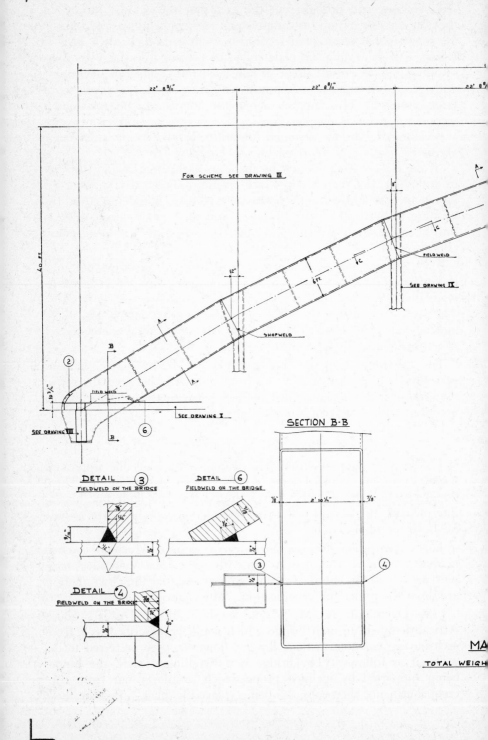

SECTION B·B

DETAIL ③
FIELDWELD ON THE BRIDGE

DETAIL ⑥
FIELDWELD ON THE BRIDGE

DETAIL ④
FIELDWELD ON THE BRIDGE

Figure 34

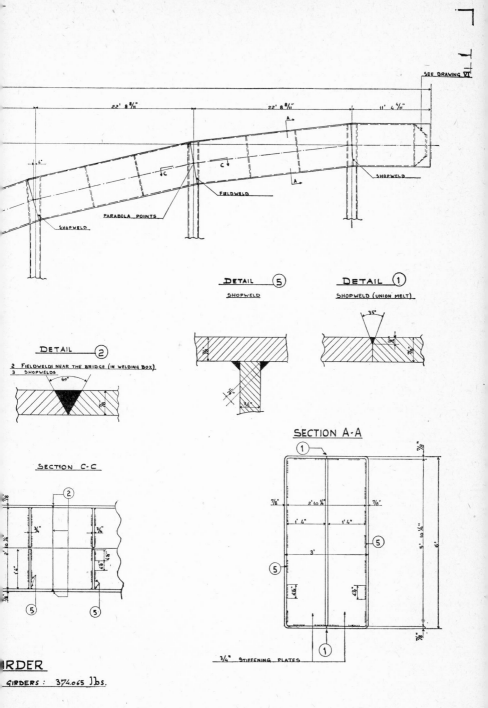

SEE DRAWING VI

22' 8 9/11"   22' 8 9/11"   11' 4 4/11"

4"

C

C

A

A

FIELDWELD

SHOPWELD

PARABOLA POINTS

SHOPWELD

DETAIL (5)
SHOPWELD

DETAIL (1)
SHOPWELD (UNION MELT)

35°

DETAIL (2)
2 FIELDWELDS NEAR THE BRIDGE (IN WELDING BOX)
3 SHOPWELDS

60°

SECTION A·A

(1)   7/8"

7/8"   2' 10 1/2"   7/8"

1' 4"   1' 4"

(5)

3'   5' 10 1/2"   6'

SECTION C·C

(2)

3/4"   3/4"

4 1/2"

(5)   (5)

(5)   4 1/2"   4 1/2"

(5)

(1)

7/8"

3/4" STIFFENING PLATES   (1)

RDER

GIRDERS : 374.065 lbs.

Figure 34 (Concluded)

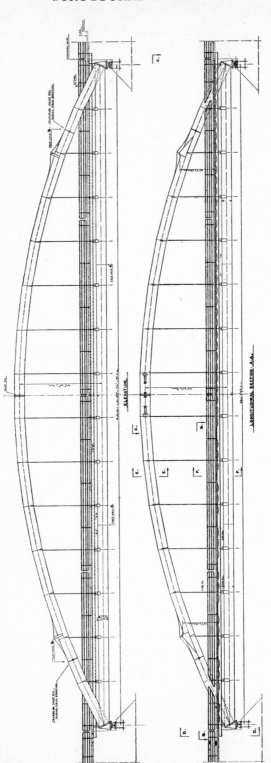

Figure 35

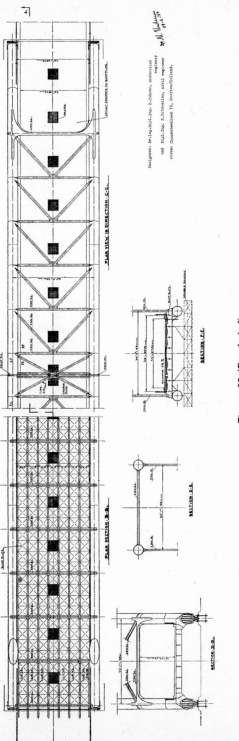

Figure 35 (Concluded)

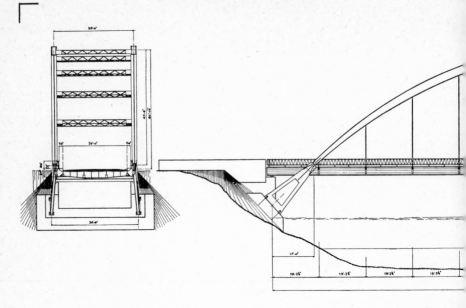

Figure 36

props are an integral part of this design and because the hinges a
not located at the ends, the bridge is discussed here rather than wi
the "Two-Hinged Arches."

The props were designed as columns, fixed and anchored at t
abutments. The length of the props was selected long enough to d
crease the span and weight of the arch rib between the hinges but n
too long because of the greater moment that would exist in the prop
The pins are situated 17 ft. inward from the ends. Also they are,
stated: "above deck level and within view of the users of the brid
to correct an impression of weakness likely to be created by the appea
ance of the arch rib decreasing in depth towards the ends of the spa
This impression is corrected by a view of the prop widening towar
its base."

Messrs. Daymond and Zakrzewski said:

"Before commencing the actual design, an extensive investigatic
was carried out into the economy of the arch. For the span of 250
the factors investigated were: type of section, rise to span ratio, ar
depth of rib.

"The following types of sections were tried, the conditions applic
approximately to those at the arch crown: I section, box section, ci
cular tube section, and elliptical tube section. The last two were di
carded as the weight for a given allowable stress was considerab
greater than for the first two. The box section was finally selecte
because, although slightly heavier than the I section, the anti-bucklin

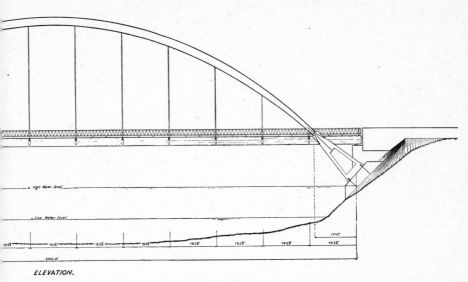

ELEVATION.

Figure 36 (Concluded)

and lateral bracing provisions would be less severe, an important factor where slenderness is being sought in the long span."

The results of these investigations led to the final design. The flange width is 30 in. The arch rib depth between quarter points is 40 in. and decreases towards the pins from 40 in. to 18 in. The distance between the vertical webs is 18 in. The lateral bracing between the ribs consists of struts which are double-plane trusses made from tubing.

As shown in Figure 36, the floor system is divided into thirteen panels and the rise of the arch above the pins is 45 ft.-4 in. Figure 37 shows the details of the prop and arch rib, as well as those for the hangers, lateral bracing, and floor system. The hangers are rods, 2⅝ in. in diameter. The deck flooring consists of ¼-in. dished plates covered with a variable, but relatively thin covering of high grade concrete. The authors said: "The plates and concrete are required as an integral part of the deck in resisting moments and thrusts, the necessary bond between the steel plating and the concrete being developed by the insertion in the concrete of special expanded metal welded to the plating."

A patent on this design has been applied for.

K. W. Dobert, Troy, New York, presented the design of a fixed arch with a rise at the center of 42 ft.-2 in. The large rectangular arch ribs are close together between portals and splayed toward the abutments as shown in Figure 38. The ribs are 30 in. wide and 54 in. deep, using three, ¾-in. plates for each flange and two, ¾-in. plates for each web. Between the portals, the arch ribs are braced together at the panel points by rectangular struts having the same width and depth as the ribs but with a single ¾-in. plate used for each flange and web.

Because the arch ribs converge from the abutments, the hangers slope outward from the arch ribs and are connected to curved brackets which are attached to the floorbeams. This arrangement is shown in each of the four sections of Figure 39.

Mr. Dobert described the appearance of his bridge in this manner:

"A four legged, vaulting, stable, arch structure whose function is to leap across the span and become a ridge backbone to support the heavy underslung weight.

"The main arch form may be compared to the human body on all fours spanning across a small stream with a weight hanging from the stomach.

"The compound curves provide a pleasing appearance from any angle of approach.

"The 'theme' of the bridge consisting of the two supporting arches which meet and are joined together are symbolic of welding, the process used to make the structure possible.

"The eye can depict the functions of the bridge members. The arch is massive, box like, and concentrated to receive the tremendous thrusts whereas the suspenders are light to resist tension.

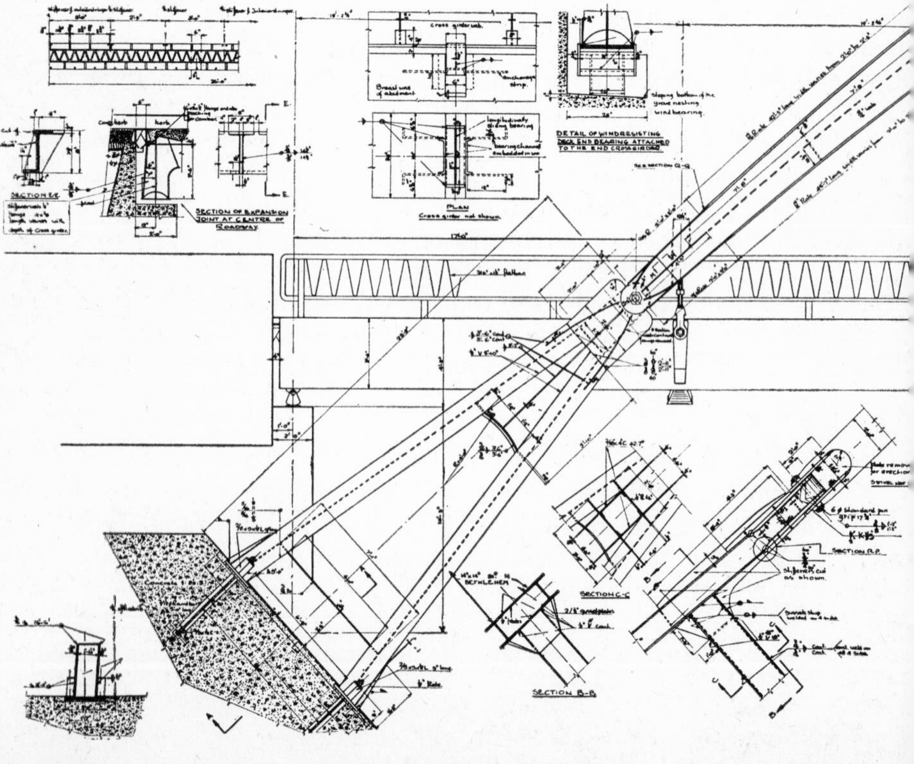

Figure 39.

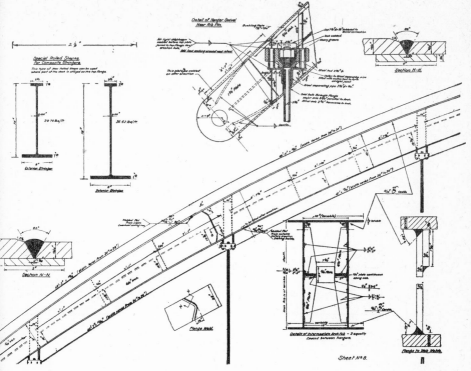

Figure 37 (Continued)

"The upper and lower hangers are transitional members between the arches and floorbeams.

"The interior of the bridge is completely free from all bracing and trusswork. All members of the bridge are minimum.

"The lower hangers, sidewalk and curbs have been moulded for harmony with the overhead structures. The bridge floor and sidewalks are wide and clear throughout the span.

"The continuous pipe railings accentuate and provide horizontality to the span."

The floor system is divided in sixteen panels. Except for longitudinal rolled beams located at the edges of the roadway, the deck is a composite structural slab composed of a ⅜-in. corrugated plate and a concrete slab additionally reinforced with both longitudinal and transverse bars. No lateral bracing system is necessary.

G. A. Foster, Barberton, Ohio, designed the unusual structure shown in Figure 40. About it, he said:

"The truss as designed is a rigid framed type of tied arch in which the radial inclination of the diagonals and the excess moment of inertia in the bottom chord combine with the rigid framing to decentralize and greatly reduce the moments that usually occur in the arch rib.

"A number of advantages occur with this design.

   1. A greater concentration of metal in the bottom chord which

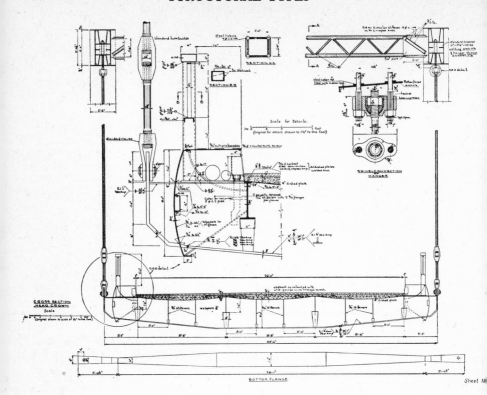

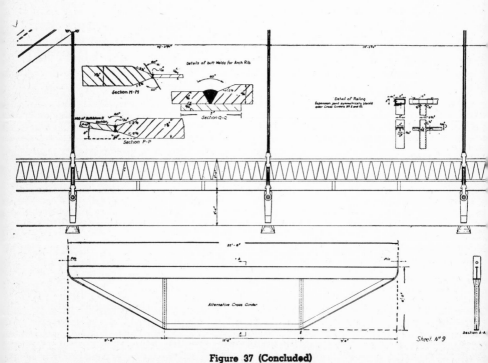

Figure 37 (Concluded)

is advantageous from a fatigue standpoint.

2. Much simplification, duplication and ease of shop fabrication.
   a. There is no drilling in any main material.
   b. Nineteen identical members consitute the total of the bracing.
   c. Twelve identical members form the upper top chord.
   d. All floor beams are identical.
   e. All stringers are plain material with no shop work required.
   f. The upper end of all diagonals are identical.

3. A compatibility with welding. Welding experience indicates that all welded end connections should be nearly fixed or nearly free. Welding makes full moment connections possible. Rigid frame construction requires full moment connections.

4. A better portal system in that a rigid connection shoves the point of inflection in the unbraced area of the passageway closer to the floor.

5. Less L/r reduction factors due to the creation of points of inflection.

6. An offset location of the interior floorbeams at much simplification of design detail, fabrication, and erection.

7. Low maintenance cost due to elimination of simple end connections which are frequent points of fatigue failure in welded work.

8. Good appearance. An arch is always effective in this respect and the beam sections add depth and strength to the appearance of individual members.

9. This design affords a positional and dimensional accuracy for all parts connected with weld and much saving in labor at some cost in material which is in line with present day labor and material cost ratios.

10. The heavy beam section used for the bottom chord enables the indicated erection procedure.

11. The cross stringers enable the entire floor system to act somewhat like a diaphragm.

Details of the upper and lower connections for the radial hangers are shown in Figure 41, also the connections of the lateral and sway bracing. These bracing struts (14 WF 87) are located away from the intersections of the hangers with arch rib as shown in Figure 40. The arch ribs and radial hangers are 24 WF sections and the bottom tie (or chord) is a 36 WF 150.

The deck is a 7/16-in. checkered floor plate which is stiffened between stringers by transverse channels welded to the underneath side of the plate.

F. G. Hayes, Pietermaritzburg, South Africa, used hangers which are inclined within a vertical plane in the design of a tied, three-

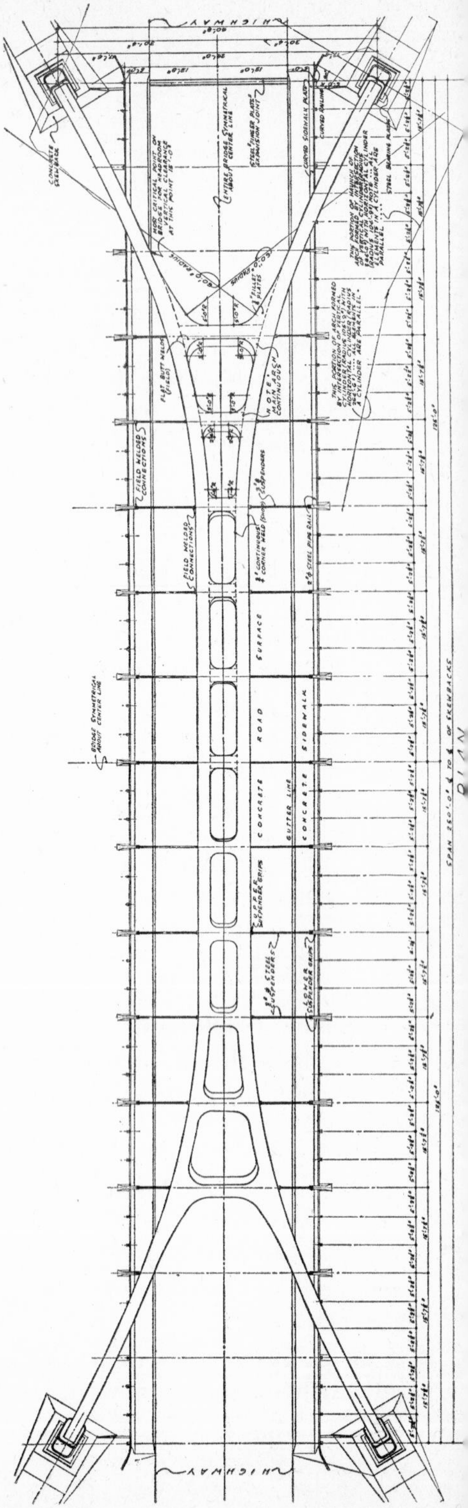
HIGHWAY
CONCRETE ROAD SURFACE
GUTTER LINE
CONCRETE SIDEWALK
FIELD WELDED CONNECTIONS
LOWER SUSPENDER GRIPS
UPPER SUSPENDER GRIPS
BRIDGE SYMMETRICAL ABOUT CENTER LINE
CONCRETE SKEWBACK
HIGHWAY
PLAN

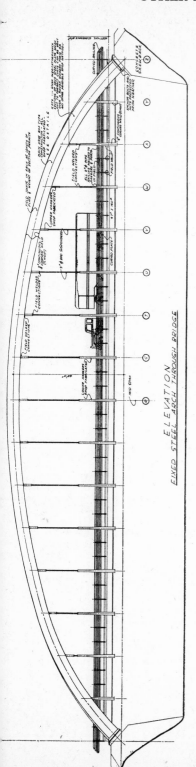

Figure 38 (Concluded)

ELEVATION
FIXED STEEL ARCH THROUGH BRIDGE

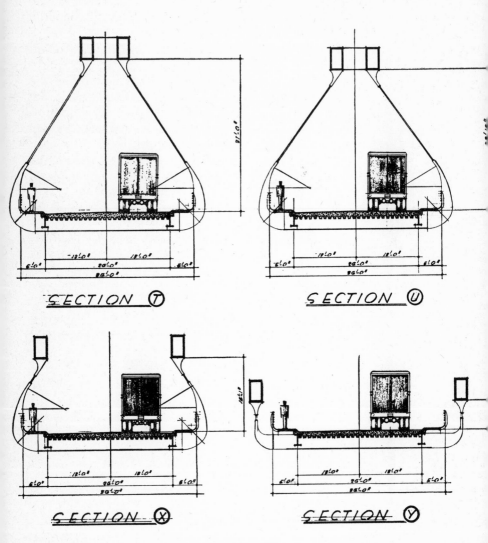

Figure 39

hingéd arch bridge. He discussed the action of the arch as follows:

"Basically the arch is a three-pinned structure having a pin at each springing point and one at the crown. The roadway or tie is articulated and suspended from the arch by inclined hangers.

"The hangers are attached to the tie at the node points and radiate from these points at equal angles to the vertical but in opposite directions.

"Under dead load all the hangers are equally loaded and are in tension.

"Under live load the tie deflects depending on the position of the load and due to the deflection of the tie the stress in hangers in the unloaded portion have the stress in them reversed and depending on the relation of dead to live load may become in a state of compression.

"To produce this state, a horizontal force must act in the tie at each node point and the force acts in such a manner as to restore the equilibrium of the structure and consequently reduce the moments in the arch."

The arch ribs are box sections varying in depth from 24 in. at the crown to 30 in. at springing. The webs are ⅜ in. thick. The flange plates are 21 in. wide and varying in thickness from ⅝ in. at the crown to 1⅛ in. at the springing. The lateral bracing between the arch ribs consists of twelve struts, each composed of two, 12-in. channels tied together by stay plates every 2 ft.-9 in.

The tie is also a box section with two, 24-in. web plates ⅜ in. thick and two flange plates 12 in. wide; however, the bottom is 1 in. thick and the top is ½ in. thick. The top plate is thinner because it acts with the reinforced concrete deck slab as a composite structure. The cross beams also act structurally with the deck slab and they likewise have larger bottom flanges than top flanges. These cross beams are spaced at about 7 ft.-7 in. centers.

The inclined hangers are 1⅜-in. galvanized wire rope. The longitudinal section of Figure 42 shows the inclination of these hangers.

Trusses

Twenty-six per cent of the participants chose the truss as the structural type for their bridges. Except for the two-hinged arches, the truss designs exceed all others in number.

The kinds of trusses are many including Pratt, Warren, and bowstring. The top chords may be horizontal, circular, parabolic between hips, or parabolic between abutments. For some of these curved chord trusses, it is difficult to decide whether they are trusses with curved chords or arches with inclined hangers.

The floor systems in these trusses, as in the other classifications, are

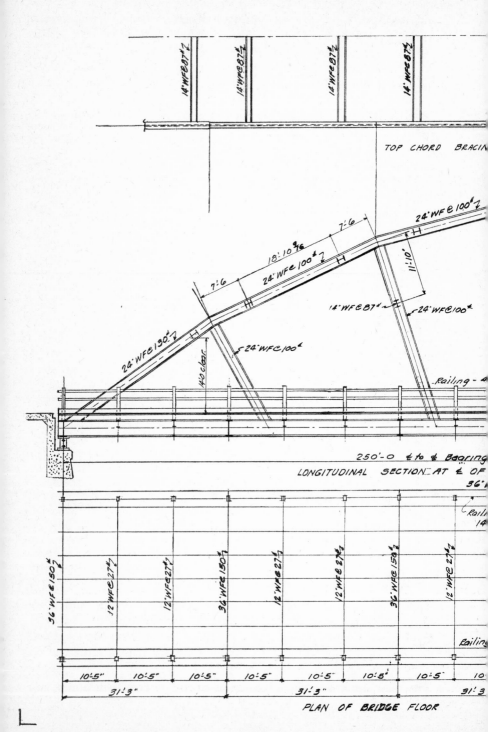

LONGITUDINAL SECTION AT ℄ OF

PLAN OF BRIDGE FLOOR

Figure 40

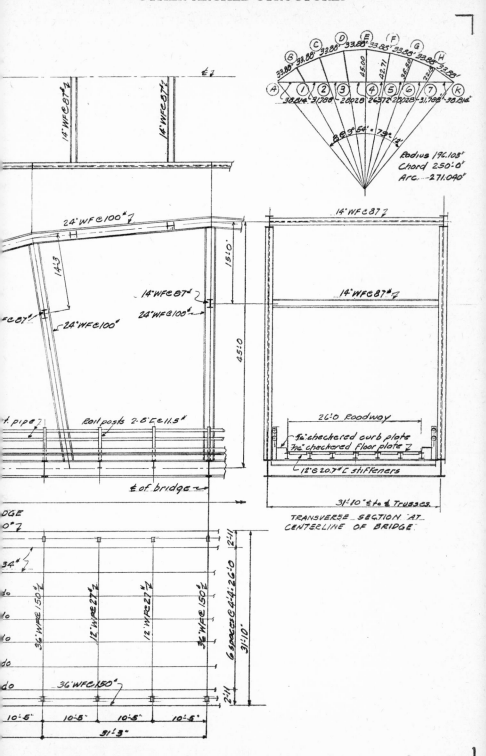

TRANSVERSE SECTION AT
CENTERLINE OF BRIDGE

Figure 40 (Concluded)

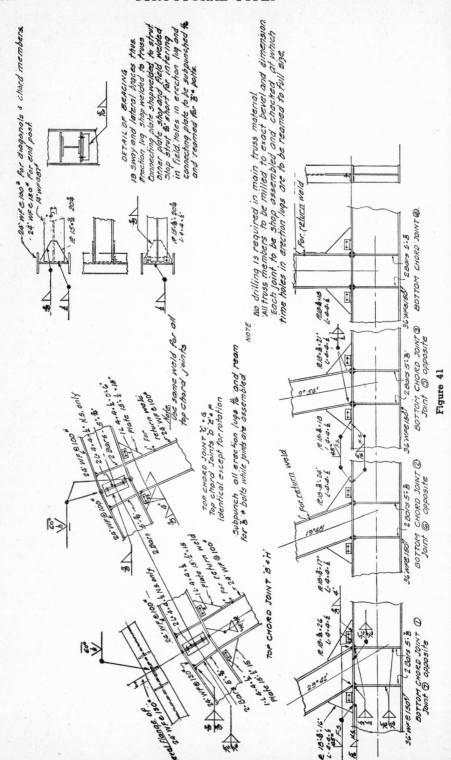

Figure 41

as varied as the primary structures. Some roadways are steel plates, others are reinforced concrete, and still others are steel grids.

J. E. Kayser, Roseland, New Jersey, submitted the design of a curved chord Pratt truss of ten panels having a center height of 35 ft. Every member of the two trusses is composed of two new tees and either a web plate or a group of tie plates. The web plate or tie plates are welded between the webs of the two tees. The flanges are vertical in position. All members of the trusses are 14 in. wide.

About his design, Mr. Kayser said: "This design is based on the gradual distribution of stress by the use of T sections of constant flange thickness, fabricated into members of constant width, thus eliminating eccentricity and holding changes in cross section to a minimum at the welded connections.

"Although the various members could be fabricated from plate, the T sections in addition to being a very flexible shape for welded design, offer the advantage of having stiffness about both axes, thus preventing dishing-in when being welded to the web, and also permitting the use of open webs of lattice bar or tie plate construction for some of the members, thereby reducing the weight of the structure as a whole.

"The welded truss has been designed with the least number of members practical, even at the sacrifice of some weight saving, in order to present a neat and trim appearance and to keep maintenance costs at a minimum. The curved connection plates are used for the better distribution of stress and for appearance.

"Maintenance costs—particularly painting—should be below average due to the small amount of members, the absence of rivets, and the easy accessibility of all parts of all members."

Figure 43 shows the size of all truss members and both the top and bottom lateral bracing systems. Figure 44 shows the connection details at two joints.

The deck is a corrugated plate, $\frac{3}{16}$ in. thick and $3\frac{3}{16}$ in. deep. It is filled and covered with asphalt paving. The corrugations are stabilized transversely by narrow, thin steel strips welded across the top and across the bottom. This deck is supported by stringers (18 WF 50) every 3 ft.-3 in.

Sidney Rochlin, Los Angeles, California, discussed the type of bridge he selected in the following words:

"The bridge is made up of 10 panels of 25 ft. each. The shape of the top chord might be termed a cross between a Pratt and a Camelback. This shape avoids on the one hand the poor appearance of the first and the excessive depth of the latter. By placing the first four upper-chord points L_0, U_1, U_2 and U_3 on the curve of an ellipse tangent to the horizontal portion at point U_3 a pleasing appearance

Point	x'	y'
0	125·0	40·0
1	113·60	39·49
2	102·24	38·69
3	90·88	37·04
4	79·52	34·73
5	68·16	31·75
6	56·80	28·13
7	45·44	23·81
8	34·08	18·81
9	22·72	13·23
10	11·36	6·93

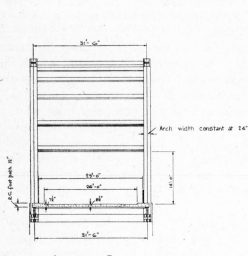

Arch width constant at 24″

CROSS SECTION

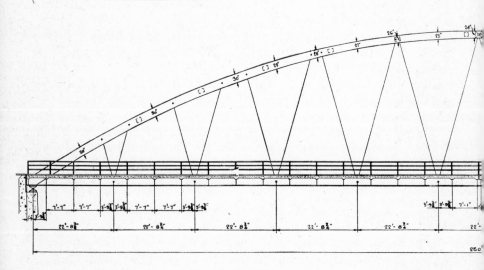

LONGITUDINA

Figure 42

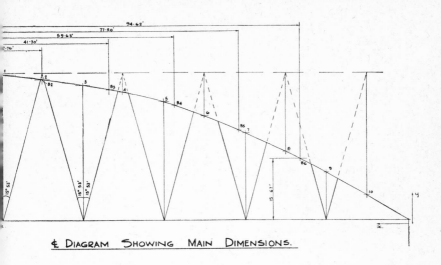

₡ Diagram Showing Main Dimensions.

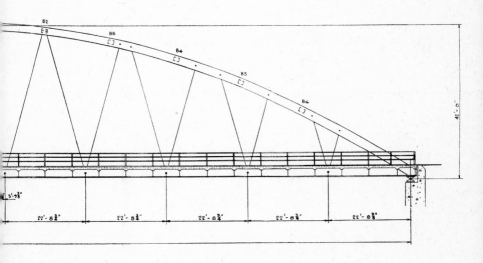

Section

Figure 42 (Concluded)

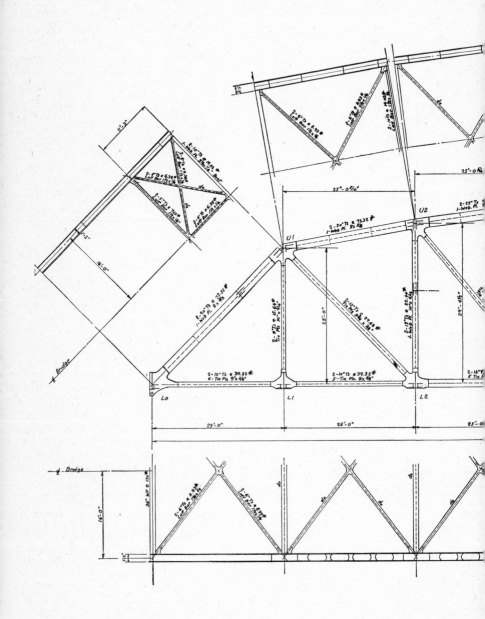

Figure 43

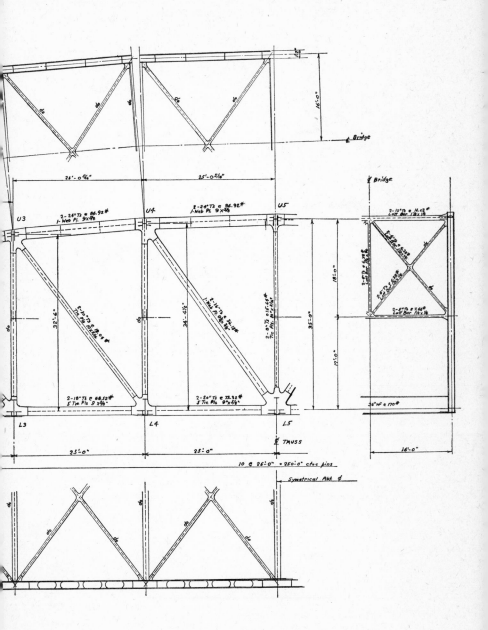

Figure 43 (Concluded)

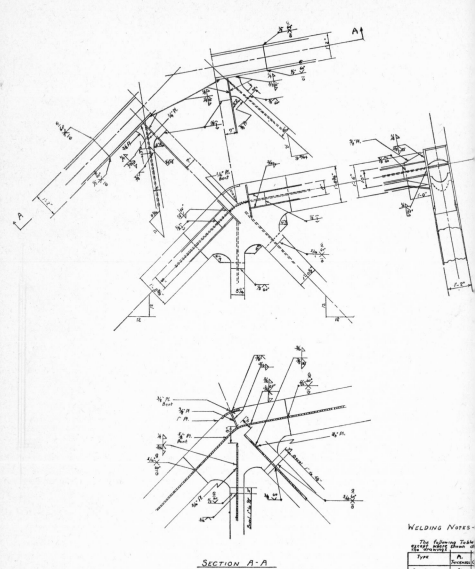

SECTION A-A

CONNECTION AT U1

WELDING NOTES—

The following Table
except where shown on
the drawings

Type	Pl. Thickness
Sq. Edge	3/16
	1/4
Single V	1/4
	5/16
	3/8
	1/2
Double V	5/8
	1
Single Bevel	1/4
	5/16
	3/8
Double Bevel	1/2"
	5/8"
	1"

Figure 44

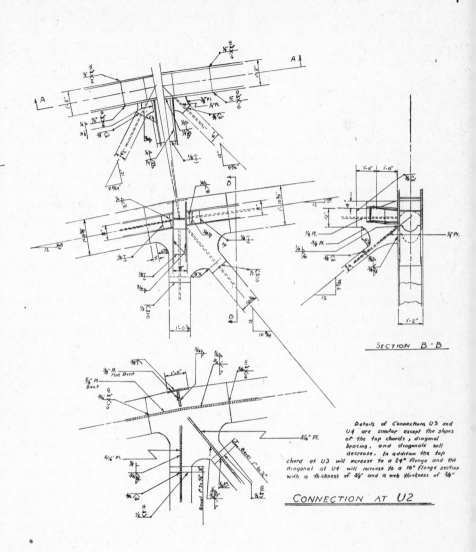

SECTION B-B

Details of Connections U3 and U4 are similar except the shapes of the top chords, diagonal bracing, and diagonals will decrease. In addition the top chord at U3 will increase to a 24" flange and the diagonal at U4 will increase to a 16" flange section with a thickness of 5/8 and a web thickness of 3/8"

CONNECTION AT U2

SECTION A-A

Sq. Edge, Single and Double Bevel and V Groove Butt Welds shall be chipped or flame gouged on the underside of the top weld and welded. (Welded from both sides)

250' SPAN HIGHWAY BRIDGE

DETAILS OF TRUSS CONNECTIONS

Figure 44 (Concluded)

is given to the ends and at the same time uniformity leading to duplication of detail is achieved for the central portion. By reducing the
depth of this central portion from what it would be in the case of a
Camelback, better L/r values may be obtained with less difficulty for
the web members. While, of course, making the bridge shallower
results in heavier chord members, the appearance achieved is more in
line with the tendency to avoid the deep gawky-looking structures
of the past.

"Instead of using a K-type arrangement of web members a lateral
strut which approximately cuts in half the lengths of all these members is used. This strut is not carried entirely through as it is not
required at the ends. This strut has a two fold advantage:

1st. In comparison with a K-type truss it eliminates a stressed
connection in each panel and avoids the long compression member. In comparison with a regular Pratt truss it makes possible
the use of a light H section rather than a latticed member or a very
heavy H section.

2nd. In comparison with these other methods the total amount
of steel and welding is appreciably less.

"Some may argue that the web members should be designed without
having to depend on a strut for lateral bracing. We feel, however,
that this is a mistaken view. The widespread use of such a simple
member as an H section which has the r in one direction greater
than that in the other can be greatly developed through the use of
such struts. There is no reason why, in a deeper bridge, two such
horizontal struts could not be used.

"The entire bridge, with minor exceptions, is constructed out of
WF sections. The use of these sections will go hand in hand with
the greater use of the arc welding process and the further development
of design ideas that will come with it."

As shown in elevation of Figure 45 and the joint details of Figure
46, all truss members are connected without the use of gusset plates.
Mr. Rochlin discusses these details as follows:

"The principal feature of the bridge lies in the method of effecting
the field connection at the truss joints. The ends of the web members
are not coped. Bearing for the web is provided for by shop welding
a plate between the flanges of the chord. This plate is punched with
3 holes to permit bolting with a small lap plate which is welded to
the end of the web member. Since the distance between the inner
faces of practically all the 14 WF series is identical, no problem is
presented in providing bearing for the flanges.

"By means of this type of connection:

1. All loads are concentric.

2. The entire cross section of the member is uniformly engaged.

3. No holes need be punched in the WF members, and no copes are necessary.

4. Easy field bolting for holding the members in position is provided.

5. The amount of welding is fixed and need not be calculated.

6. All the field welds are in exposed positions.

7. Except for the cross section of the web, there is no duplicate welding.

*   *   *

"Small variations in the clear distance between flanges of the chord may be corrected by means of jacks at the time that the web connection plates are installed.

"One minor disadvantage of the joint lies in the fact that there is an undrained pocket between the webs intersecting at the bottom chord. This may be corrected either by filling with bituminous roof putty or some other suitable material, or else providing a drain hole in the plate. In these joints we have provided a drain hole. Where pockets occur in the sway bracing, or elsewhere, the first method has been used."

Basil Sourochnikoff, Wilmington, Delaware, considered both a truss and a tied arch. His discussion of these types and of the truss having a parabolic upper chord which he selected is presented as follows:

"It will be assumed that the site conditions and cost of foundations are such that a structure on simple supports is justified in spite of the fact that it may be heavier than an indeterminate structure causing horizontal trusts at supports. This limits the choice of the structure to two general types: (1) A truss on simple supports and (2) A tied arch. The relative merits of these two types and of the composite structure used in the design are discussed in what follows.

"*Truss.* It is well known that welded trusses do not have the same fatigue strength as riveted trusses of substantially the same design, and that this fact has proved to be an impediment to the use of welded trusses for bridges. Tests have shown that the weak point is generally at the juncture of truss members to gussets (see for example: 'Fatigue of Welded and Riveted Trusses' by C. Cerardini in the Welding Journal Supplement of June 1949.) The weakness is undoubtedly due to heavy stress concentrations which occur at gussets due to secondary bending and sudden change in section. It may be overcome either by increasing the strength (and therefore the stiffness) of the connections, or by attempting to reduce the secondary bending moment which is the prime cause of the weakness. In both cases a sudden change of section must be avoided. Various connection details have been designed in the attempt to increase the strength of connections, but, being rather involved, they have generally remained unpopular

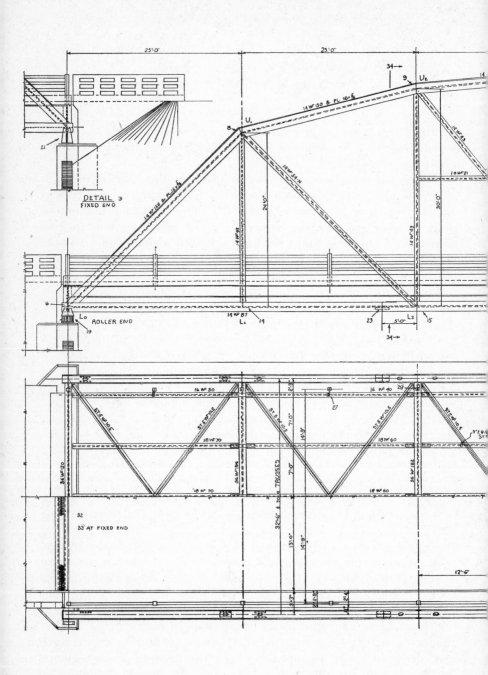

Figure 45

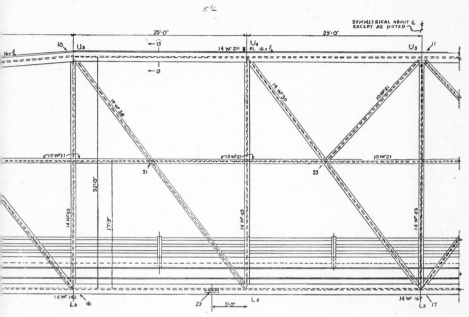

ELEVATION 1

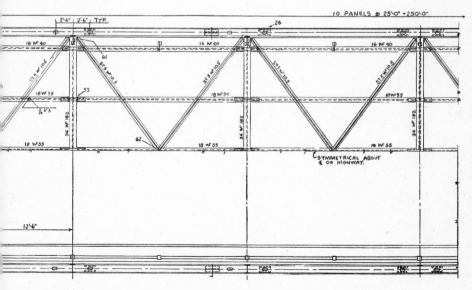

PLAN 2

Figure 45 (Concluded)

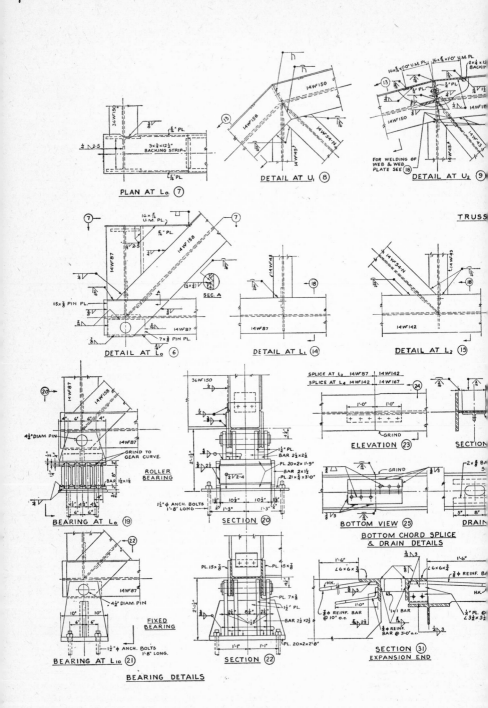

PLAN AT L₀ ⑦

DETAIL AT U₁ ⑧

DETAIL AT U₂ ⑨

TRUSS

DETAIL AT L₀ ⑥

DETAIL AT L₁ ⑭

DETAIL AT L₂ ⑮

ROLLER BEARING

BEARING AT L₀ ⑲

FIXED BEARING

BEARING AT L₁₀ ㉑

BEARING DETAILS

SECTION ⑳

SECTION ㉒

ELEVATION ㉓

SECTION

BOTTOM VIEW ㉕

DRAIN

BOTTOM CHORD SPLICE
& DRAIN DETAILS

SECTION ㉛
EXPANSION END

Figure 46

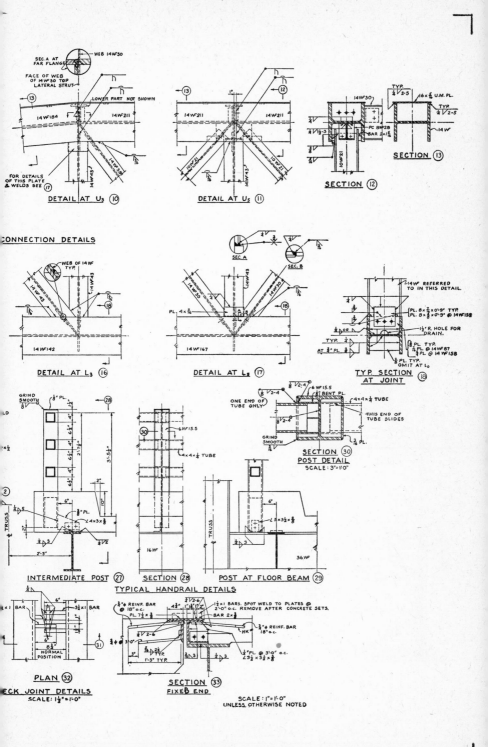

Figure 46 (Concluded)

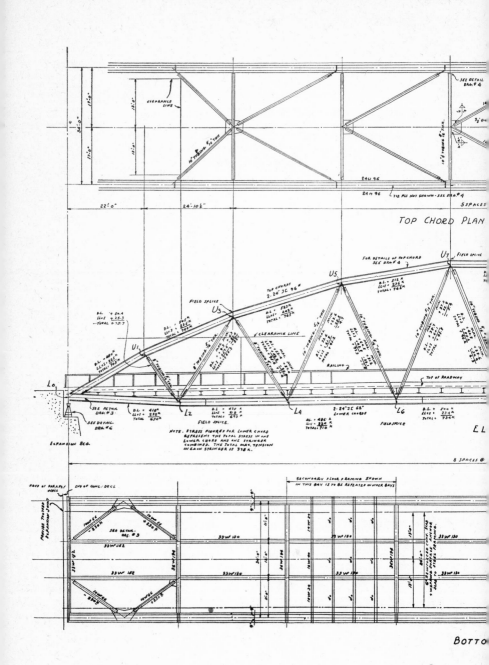

Figure 47

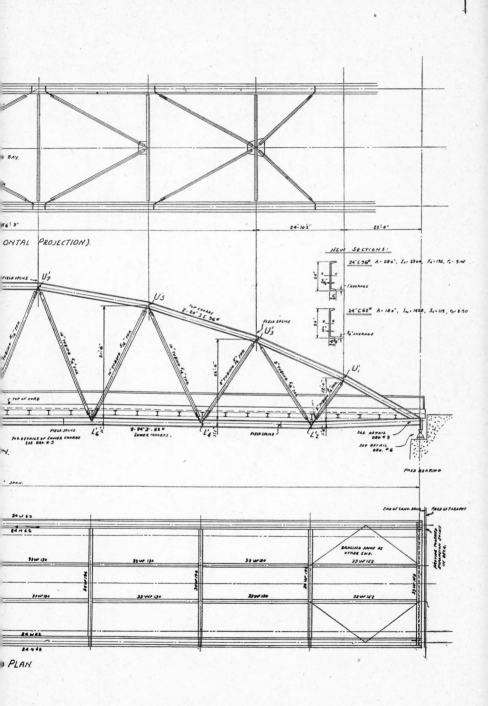

Figure 47 (Concluded)

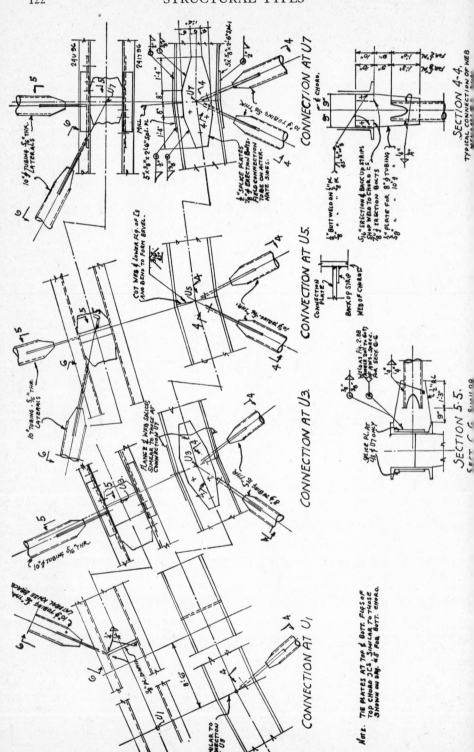

CONNECTION AT U7.

SECTION 4-4.
TYPICAL CONNECTION OF WEB

CONNECTION AT U5.

CONNECTION AT U3.

SECTION 5-5.

CONNECTION AT U1.

Note: THE PLATES AT TOP & BOTT. P4S OF
TOP CHORD 2C5. SIMILAR TO THOSE
SHOWN ON DWG. 4.5 FOR BOTT. CHORD.

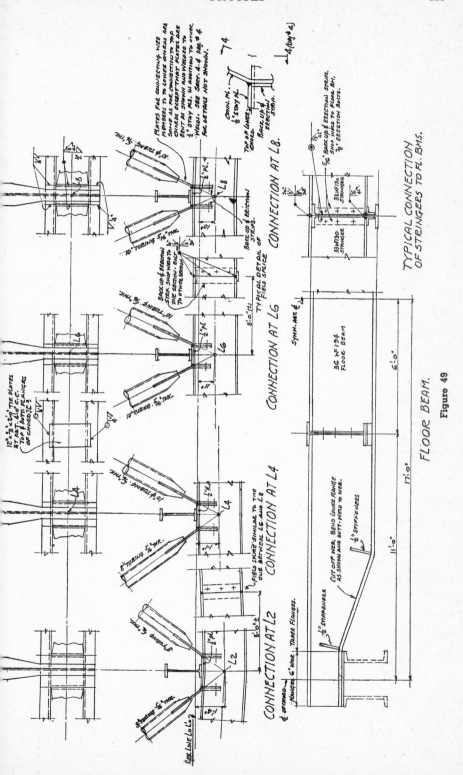

CONNECTION AT L2

CONNECTION AT L4

CONNECTION AT L6

CONNECTION AT L8

TYPICAL CONNECTION
OF STRINGERS TO FL. BMS.

FLOOR BEAM.

Figure 49

with American contractors. It seems therefore justifiable to direct the attention towards reducing the secondary bending moment in the connections which can be done by avoiding sub-paneling and short and stubby members, and by designing connections in such a way as to provide a certain amount of flexibility in the plane of the truss without impairing their resistance to normal forces.

"*Tied Arch.* In the tied arch, the web members (hangers) are considerably more slender than those of a truss with parallel chords and receive a smaller load. Their connection to the chords presents less of a problem than the connection of web members of the truss. The live load, however, produces a reversing bending moment in the chords. This is obviously an undesirable feature, especially that in a 250-ft. span with a fairly light deck, the effect of the moment is not adequately offset by the direct forces.

"*Structure Used in the Present Design.* This structure may be regarded as either a tied arch with inclined hangers, or as a truss with a closely parabolic upper chord. The advantage it presents over the arch is that the bending moment in the chords due to moving live load is practically eliminated because of the trussing effect of the inclined hangers. On the other side, the vertical component of the stress in the upper chord relieves the stress in the web members with the effect that these members may be made considerably more slender than in a truss with parallel chords. The maximum stress in the web members is a tension as it would be in the hangers of an arch. Calculations show that the reversal due to the passage of live load is quite small and does not exceed one-third of the maximum tension. Therefore, the connections of web members to chords present less of a problem than in a truss with parallel chords and the secondary bending is reduced on account of greater flexibility of web members, with the effect that welding may be used to a greater advantage and the life of connections prolonged. To appreciate the advantage more fully, one must note that in a 250-ft. span the connections of web members to chords are necessarily made in field on account of the length of the members, and that therefore the importance of field work is reduced by using the proposed design. It is true, of course, that the total stress in the upper chord does not decrease towards the ends from the maximum at mid-span as it does in a truss with parallel chords, so that the average section of the upper chord is greater and connections and splices are larger. It must be noted, though, that chords carry a relatively steady non-reversing load and therefore welded connections may be used to advantage."

Both the top chord and the bottom chord are composed of two, 24-in. channels which are suggested new shapes. Each channel weighs

96 lb. per ft. for the top chord, 62 lb. per ft. for the bottom chord. There are two continuous stringers in the floor system. Horizontal braces in the end panels (see Figure 47) serve to make both of these stringers act as effective bottom chord material.

The web members of the truss and the members of the top lateral bracing system are either 8-in. or 10-in. tubes. At the ends, these tubes are slotted and welded in the shop to a plate located in a plane perpendicular to the plane of the truss. These single plates are in turn welded in the field to the backs of the chord channels. This detail makes possible the flexible connection shown in Figure 48.

Figure 49 shows the two floor stringers which support the 6-in. reinforced concrete slab and the manner in which the floorbeams are supported on top of the bottom chord.

Ivar Grove, Oslo, Norway, designed a truss bridge having the top chord curved in a circular arc. Many engineers refer to a structure of this kind as a bowstring truss. The web system is of the Warren type with no verticals. There are 12 panels. The top and bottom chord members for this type of truss must be designed to resist bending moments as well as axial loads. Both chords are made of beams. The top chord is 20 in. deep and has flanges that are 20 in. wide. The bottom chord is 24 in. deep and has flanges that are 12 in. wide. The truss diagonals are pipes, 8 in. in diameter. The members bracing the top chords are 6-in. pipes. They form a double intersection lateral system without struts. The arrangement of the trusses and the bracing is shown in Figure 50.

A prestressed concrete slab serves as the entire floor system including the lateral bracing for the bottom chords. Figure 51 shows a transverse section of the bridge.

M. M. Clayton, Portland, Oregon, presented the design of what he termed a "Diamond Truss" bridge. The name originates from the shape of the members of the truss. All truss members are composed of two angles arranged in a diamond configuration. This arrangement permits the use of single gusset plates at each joint. The equal leg angles utilized in making these diamond shapes include some proposed new sizes. The top and bottom chords are made of 18-in. angles, the diagonals of 12-in. angles, and the verticals of 8-in. angles.

The bridge is a non-parallel Warren truss with a height of 40 ft. at the center of the span. There are ten panels in the truss. An elevation of the truss and a plan of the top lateral bracing is shown in Figure 52.

The top lateral bracing, the bottom lateral bracing, and the handrails are designed with members of this diamond shape. The roadway is 5-in. I-Beam-Lok open floor supported on rolled stringers (12 WF 31)

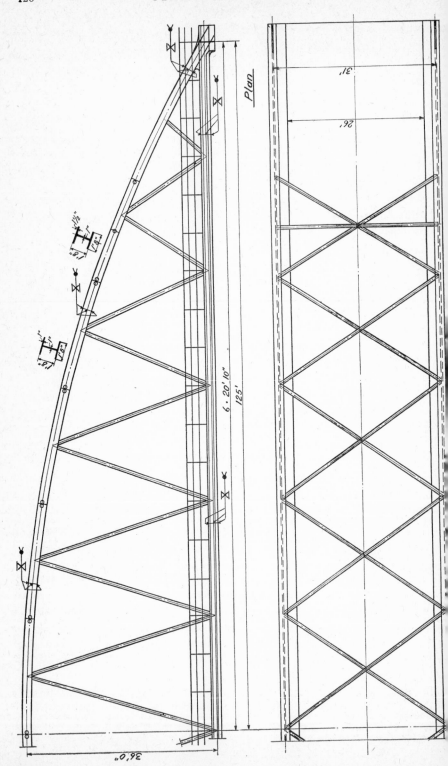

Plan

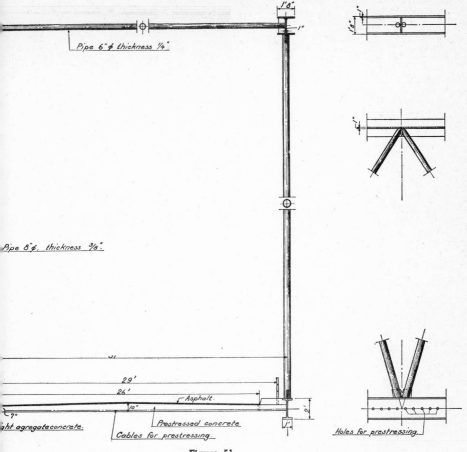

Pipe 6"ø thickness ¼".

Pipe 8"ø, thickness ⅜".

29'
26'
10"
7"
ght agregateconcrete.
Prestressed concrete
Cables for prestressing.

Holes for prestressing.

Figure 51

spaced at 3-ft. centers. The floorbeams are 33 WF 130 sections for the middle 8 ft. but taper to a 1-ft. depth at the ends. The connection of the floorbeam to the truss is below the bottom chord member.

Typical joints using the diamond shaped member are shown in Chapter V where these joints are discussed in more detail. Mr. Clayton stated that he was filing an application for a patent covering features of his design. For information on patent rights contact Mr. Clayton.

Anker Engelund, Copenhagen, Denmark, designed the bowstring truss shown in Figure 53. The truss has eight panels of equal length. The radius of the top chord is approximately 200 ft. which gives the truss a maximum height of about 44 ft.

As part of his discussion, Mr. Engelund presented the following advantages of this design.

"The particular truss which is used in this design, characterized by

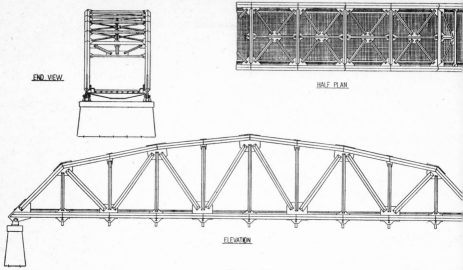

Figure 52

the circle-curved upper chord and the sloping web members without verticals, will give the following advantages:

1. The maximum-stress will be nearly constant in (a) the upper chord, (b) the lower chord, and (c) the web members, which again involves that the same section can be used in each of the three sets of members.
2. The diagonals (web members) will entirely be stressed in tension. When the live load and the dead load stresses are of opposite signs, only 70 per cent of the dead load stress is considered as effective in counteracting the live load stress.
3. The stresses in the web members being small, all of the gusset connections will also be very simple and the gusset plates themselves very little stressed.

"All of the members are designed as closed box-formed tubes which will give the following advantages:

1. Good economy with comparatively great stiffness of the members.
2. The continuous longitudinal welds (seams) in the tube members may be made by automatic welding, as these seams are not at all stressed but necessary for sealing and closing.
3. The least possible surface to be maintained.

"The main points of the design have been:

1. To make as many parts as possible quite equal.
2. To make the most possible connections in joints and at panel points quite equal (standardized details.)

"For instance the upper chord in each truss contains 6 pieces of exactly the same length and the lower chord 7 pieces of the same length. All web members (except the diagonals acting as sway bracing) have both the same sections and also exactly the same details at the connections to the gusset plates."

The sizes of the main truss members and a plan of the top lateral members are given as part of Figure 53. The struts of the top lateral system are 8-in. pipe and the diagonals are 5-in. pipe. The reinforced concrete floor slab acts as the bottom lateral bracing. Figure 54 shows the details of some of the truss connections.

A. M. Freudenthal, New York, New York, designed the bridge shown in Figure 55. It has been classified here as a bowstring truss; however, it could be referred to as a tied arch with inclined hangers arranged as the diagonals of a Warren truss. The bottom chord is cambered upward a total of 3 ft. The distance between the top and bottom chords at the center of the span is 32 ft. The end panel at each support is 27 ft. long and the 7 interior panels are 28 ft. long.

Figure 56 indicates the make-up of the top and bottom chords and the diagonals. The top chord has a 24 by 1¼-in. top flange plate, two webs 24 in. deep, and two bottom bars each 3 in. square. The webs are ½ in. thick except near the ends where the thickness is ¾ in. The bottom chord has top and bottom flange plates (18 by ⅞ in.) and a 48 by ½-in. web plate. This bottom flange plate is a "nose-plate," a plate having a special stem or stub for welding. The diagonals are 5-in. pipes except for the two diagonals at the center which are 6-in. pipes. The top chords are braced together by 7 transverse struts that are similar to the top chord but slightly smaller in size.

In Mr. Freudenthal's words, this type of design "produces a structure which embodies the advantages of both the truss and the tied arch, but avoids, or substantially reduces, their disadvantages, which are particularly objectionable in a fully welded structure. These are the higher concentrated secondary and residual thermal stresses unavoidably associated with the welded truss joints, and the high flexibility and fatigue sensitivity of the stiffening girder of the conventional tied arch resulting from the absence of dead load moments and the large amplitude of fluctuation of the live load stresses under transient loads. The high secondary and the concentrated thermal stresses in the rigid joints of fully welded trusses have been responsible for most of the reported failures of such structures under dynamic loads: their existence is the principal reason for the general prohibition of welding of joints of truss bridges, particularly in countries with the most advanced development in the techniques of structural welding, such as Sweden. In the submitted design with diagonal hanger arrange-

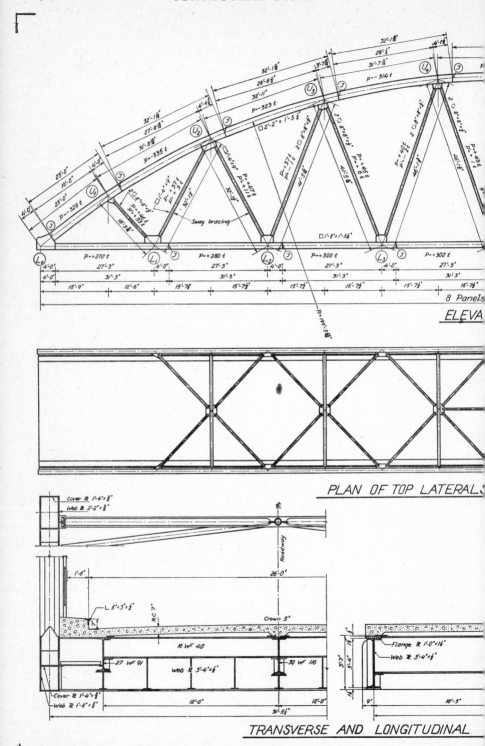

ELEVA[TION]

PLAN OF TOP LATERAL[S]

TRANSVERSE AND LONGITUDINAL

Figure 53

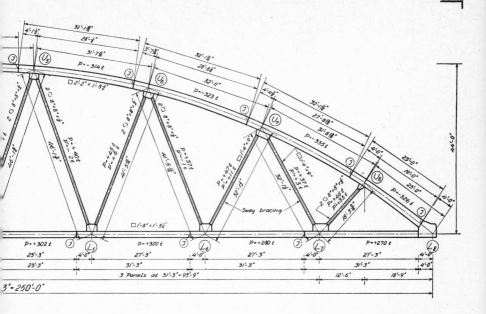

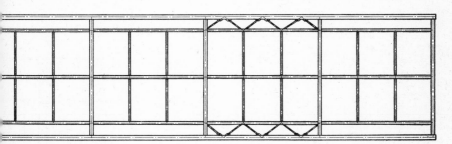

D FLOOR SYSTEM

All stresses measured in tons (1 ton = 2000 lbs)

P is maximum stress of tension or compression.
P' is the stress when the live load and dead load stresses
are of opposite sign and in this case only 70 per cent of
the dead load stress is considered as effective in counteracting the live load stress. All web members show
to be in tension.

The position of the field joints are indicated ⓙ

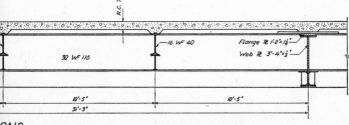

ONS

Figure 53 (Concluded)

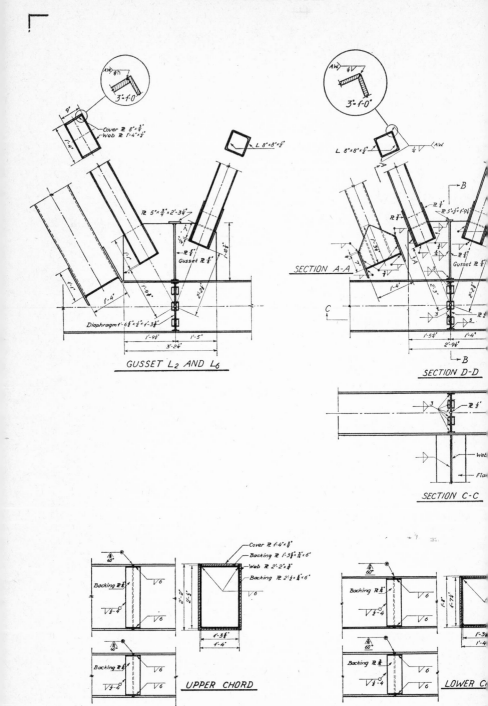

GUSSET L_2 AND L_6

SECTION A-A

SECTION D-D

SECTION C-C

UPPER CHORD

LOWER CHORD

STANDARD JOINT

Figure 54

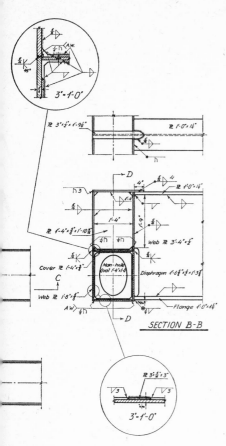

SECTION B-B

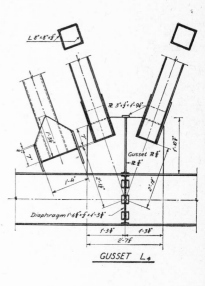

GUSSET L₄

GUSSET L₃ AND L₅

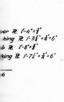

A.W. apply to the use of automatic welding.

All welds ⅜" unless otherwise noted.

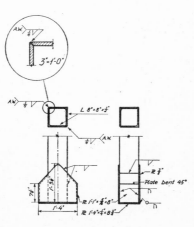

STANDARD-END OF WEB MEMBER

Figure 54 (Concluded)

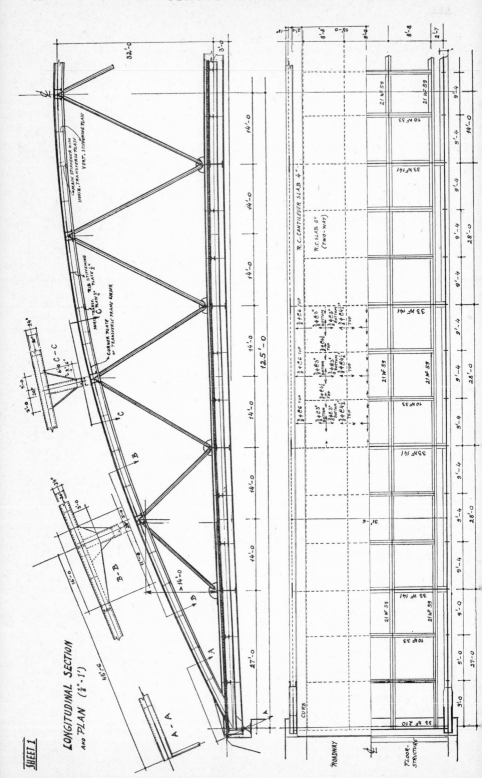

LONGITUDINAL SECTION
AND PLAN (⅛" - 1')

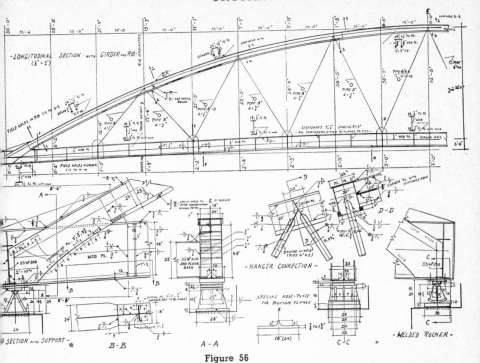

Figure 56

ment these stresses are practically eliminated by the elimination of areas of concentration of welds, by the extremely high flexibility of the 'diagonals' and the continuity of the 'chords', which are designed to carry relatively high bending moments in addition to axial loads.

"The diagonal hangers are also responsible for a very substantial reduction of the flexibility of the stiffening truss and of the amplitude of the stress reversals under transient live loads: they produce a truss-like effect with regard to both the joint action of rib and girder, and the substantial reduction of the live load bending moments in this girder, compared to those in the conventional tied arch girder with vertical hangers. The fabrication of the shallow stiffening girder—which has generally proved to be the simplest and most effective structural form for fully welded bridges—as well as of the box-shaped ribs does not present any problem in either shop or field that has not successfully been solved in the fabrication of a large number of fully welded structures and that is not at present considered a matter of simple routine. Similarly, the erection of the proposed tied arch structure is extremely simple: its principal phase is the conventional erection of two shallow web-girders on a few light supports. These girders are then connected and stiffened by the floorbeams, before the ribs and their horizontal bracing are erected on the completed girders and connected to them at the supports as well as by the hangers."

Vierendeel Trusses

Considering the fact that the number of Vierendeel trusses submitted was not large, the differences in the designs are considerable. Most of the Vierendeel trusses have curved top chords composed of straight segments between panel points. Some of the designs have chord members which vary in depth between the panel points. One structure is designed with prestressing rods in the bottom chord member. The top chord in one design is braced laterally by rigid brackets extending upward from the floorbeams. These brackets serve also as the vertical members of the Vierendeel truss.

The types of floors used in these bridges include reinforced concrete slabs, steel open gratings, special rolled steel shapes, and precast and prestressed concrete floor panels.

Arsham Amirikian, Chevy Chase, Maryland, gave this as the concept of his design:

"Conventional types of truss framing are not readily adaptable to welded construction owing to certain physical limitations inherent in their arrangement and consequent difficulties in fabrication and erection. The main objective of the proposed design is to devise a simplified framing which will eliminate these difficulties and thus encourage the use of welding in bridge framework. The desired simplification is obtained by the utilization of the framing principle known as 'Vierendeel Truss,' in a novel arrangement."

The Vierendeel truss itself and the dimensions of the "wedge-beams" used in its design are shown in Figure 57. The connection and splice details are given in Figure 58.

Mr. Amirikian described the bridge and gave the features of the framing in the following manner:

"The trusses have parallel chords, with an over-all depth of 23 ft. and a span of 250 ft., sub-divided into ten panels of 25-ft. length. The framing is featured by the shapes of the members and the locations of the splices. Each member is composed of two wedge-shaped segments, called 'wedge-beam,' which are joined together at their shallow end.

"The introduction of a splice at midspan of each member is predicated on two considerations: (a) to simplify the fabrication of the components, and (b) to enable the assembly of relatively large segments in the shop and thus minimize the work of assembly and welding in the field. The flexibility provided by this arrangement constitutes the greatest advantage of the new design. This will be readily seen by reference to the assembly and erection procedure outlined on sheet No. 3 [see Figure 96 Page 215].

"The unusual shapes of the members conform to the flexural stress pattern of the framing, which is characterized by minimum stresses

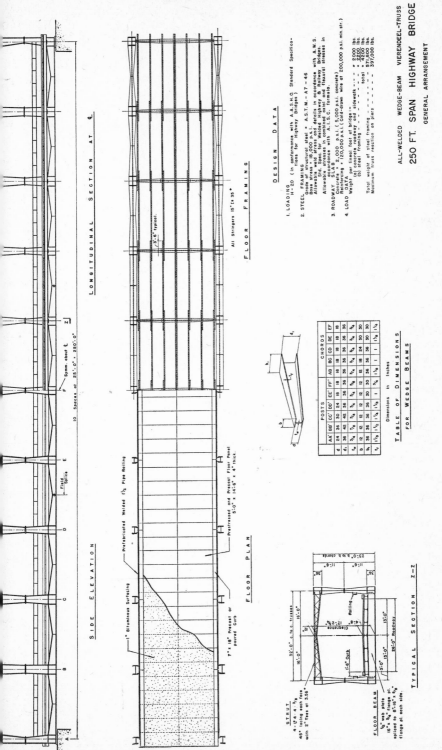

Figure 57

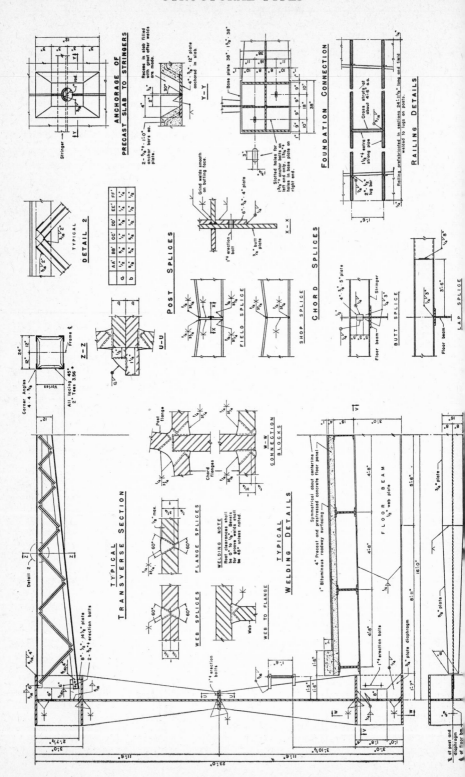

occuring at about center of each span and increasing to a maximum at the ends. While it is assumed that these sections may eventually be obtained by rolling, their welded fabrication from plating presents no difficulties. As a matter of fact, it will probably be more economical to produce them by the latter method.

"By omitting the diagonals from the webbing of the trusses, the connection problem at the joints is reduced to the simple form of a T. Unlike conventional truss framings, where at least two web members connect to the chords at each panel point, in the proposed arrangement there is but one member, namely, the post to be joined to the chords.

"It is realized that the weight of the truss is somewhat heavier than would have been if diagonals were utilized. This is a characteristic of the Vierendeel truss, due to the fact that the load is transmitted to the supports primarily by bending. However, this is only a small disadvantage which is more than counterbalanced by appreciable savings in the simplified fabrication and by the more significant savings in the cost of erection. The extent of the latter benefit is vividly reflected by the percentage of the erection cost which is estimated to be only 7 per cent of the total cost of the structure. As an added feature, the proprosed system possesses a definite esthetic advantage in presenting a clean-cut and pleasing appearance."

The top chords are braced by a strut at each panel point. Each strut consists of four angles latticed together to form a member of varying depth (see Figure 58.)

The roadway slab is made of 5-ft. widths of precast and prestressed concrete floor units having a 4-in. thickness. These units are surfaced with 1 in. of bituminous material. The slab units are interconnected and attached to the supporting stringers by welding to a series of insert plates cast into the panels.

H. H. Werner, Long Island City, New York, designed an eight panel Vierendeel truss with a curved top chord having a maximum rise of 38 ft.-3 in. The two end panels (29 ft.) are shorter than the six interior panels (32 ft.) "in order to equalize moments and reactions resulting from continuity and to give a more pleasing appearance." All members of the truss including the top chord, bottom chord and verticals are 36 WF sections; however, the weights vary from 182 to 300 lb. per ft.

The truss elevation, the top chord bracing, and the floor plan are shown in Figure 59.

The top chord bracing is made of 10 WF 33 Sections except for the members of the portal which are 14 WF sections. The diagonals of the bottom lateral bracing are 4 x 4 x ⅜ angles. The floorbeams

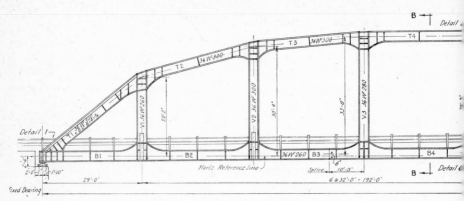

ONE HALF ELEVATION

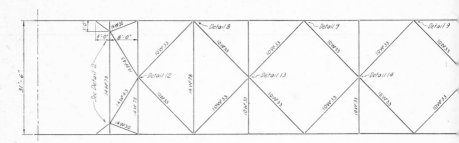

ONE HALF PLAN OF TOP CHORD BRACING

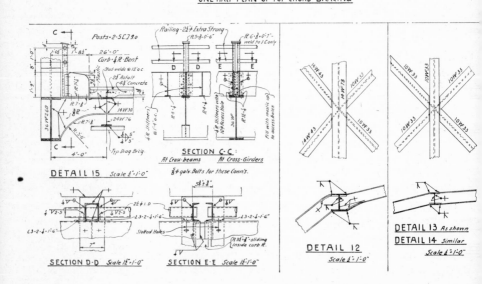

Figure 59

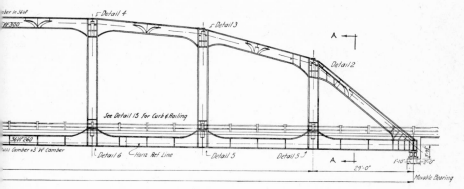

ONE HALF LONGITUTIONAL SECTION

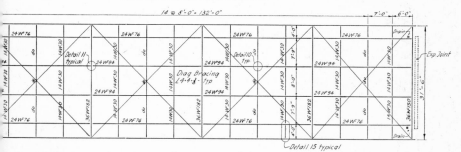

ONE HALF PLAN AT BOTTOM CHORD

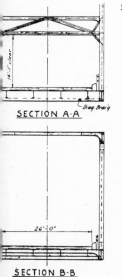

SECTION A-A

SECTION B-B

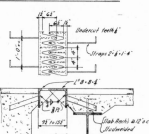

EXPANSION JOINT AT MOVABLE END

Scale 1"=1'-0"

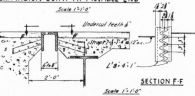

EXPANSION JOINT AT FIXED END

Scale 1"=1'-0"

SECTION F·F

GENERAL NOTES: All design, material & work to be in accord. with Std. Spec's for Highway Bridges - AASHO-1949 and Std. Spec's for Welded Highway & Railway Bridges of the Am. Welding Soc.-1947, and in special:
Steel: ASTM-A7-46 - except as noted for bearings.
Base Stress - 18000 #/□"
Welds: Am Welding Soc. Spec's -1947
Reinf. Concrete: f'c-3750 #/□", fs -16000 #/□
Masonry Bearing: 600 #/□"

Loads: D.L. - Roadway - 100 #/□' avg.
Railg & Curb - 120 #/ft ea. side
Roadway supports- 900 #/ft
One Truss - ± Brac'g - 800 #/ft
Total DL - 2670 #/ft ea. Truss
L.L. - H20-Std Truck Load or:
640 #/ft lane load - 18" or 26" conc. L.
Impact - $\frac{50}{L+125}$ or max 30%
Reactions:
D.L. Steel Structure - 160 k each
D.L. Road, Curb & Railg - 182 k "
D.L. Total - 342 k "
Max L.L. + Impact - 132 k any
Total - 478 k
Wind: 89 k Horiz each end for 2 bearings
30 k Vert. ea. bearing
longitutional: 63 k ea fixed bearing

WELDED BRIDGE
THROUGH HIGHWAY BRIDGE: 250'-0"
PLANS, SECTIONS & DETAILS
Scale ⅜"=1'-0" unless noted. Dwg. No. 1

Figure 59 (Concluded)

are 36 WF 182. There are four lines of stringers with the space between the lines being 7 ft.-9 in., 8 ft.-0 in., and 7 ft.-9 in., respectively. Between each pair of successive floorbeams are three cross girders (14 WF 30). The two-way reinforced concrete slab is supported transversely by either the cross girders or the floorbeams and longitudinally by the stringers. The slab is 4¾ in. thick with haunches of 2 in. by 6 in. at all supports. A 2½-in. asphalt surfacing for the slab is suggested.

Mr. Werner selected this type of structure for the following reasons:

"Welded connections naturally tend to be moment-connections, which are the characteristic requirement for Vierendeel trusses.

"The structure is simple, pleasing, and sturdy.

"There are few connections thus reducing shop and field work.

"Erection procedures . . . . . are simple allowing close field supervision and least obstruction of the opening which is to be spanned.

"The truss members are heavy and simple resulting in easy mainte-nance, great resistance to damage, and long life.

"It can be reinforced easily."

The main connections are streamlined and most of the welds are butt welds.

Miscellaneous Types

The bridges discussed in this classification are representative of the types of structures submitted in this Program that have not been included previously, except for a very few exceptions.

J. L. Waling, C. W. Lawton, E. M. Lewiecki, D. L. Pyke, and B. M. Radcliffe, of West Lafayette, Indiana, presented the design of a two-hinged truncated A-frame. They made the following comments about their design.

"A desirable choice of general arrangements for a welded structure is one which produces stress reversal ranges as small as possible, with the maximum stress compressive, and at the same time maintains the desired simplicity. The writers believe that their choice of arrange-ment which they like to call a two-hinged truncated A-frame is, on this basis, a good one. Figure 60 shows this arrangement. The main rib on each side is hinged at the abutments and the roadway furnishes a tie against relative longitudinal motion of the mid-height of the two sloping legs. Loads are transmitted to the ribs by floorbeams at the intersection of the roadway and the ribs and by the three floorbeam hangers which can be seen clearly in Figure 60. The roadway is provided with rockers at each abutment.

"A highway bridge engineer should never forget the motorists, most of whom prefer bridges which allow the passengers to see the reason for the bridge. A minimum of obstruction of view over the side and a maximum of protection from going over the side make for the optimum in meeting the requirements and the needs of the motorists.

*   *   *

"The truncated A-frames are box girder type construction, stiffened within by diaphragms and brackets. Access by a door at each springing allows for inspection and maintenance of the interior of each box girder. This type of construction is especially advantageous from maintenance and appearance standpoints since the bulk of the parts, which would be unsightly and hard to paint, are protected within the box and only a smooth, easily painted surface with attractive lines is exposed to the elements and to view.

"The tie provided by the floor system against relative longitudinal motion of the mid-height of the two sloping legs of each rib is quite valuable in distributing and reducing the bending moments caused by non-symmetrical loads. This participation by the floor system does not require a heavier floor than would otherwise be needed.

"The clean detail of the hanger connections to the ribs is an important advantage of the box rib construction. The lower flange of the box is spliced to the heavy diaphragms which at these points are extended below for connection to the hangers. This type of splice in the box flange is possible since the maximum tensile stresses here are small compared to the compressive stress. Furthermore it is not detrimental to the hanger strength since much more area than is required by the hanger is provided by the extended diaphragm.

"The shop fabrication of segments of these arch ribs is a very important item to be considered. Each rib is designed for shop fabrication in seven parts, requiring only six field splices of web and flange plates. This reduces field welding of these main structural members to a minimum.

"Lateral bracing of the truncated A-frames is accomplished by the upper lateral system and the lateral system under the roadway as well as by the floor system.

"The upper lateral system, which can be seen in Figure 60 consists of transverse plate girders of depth equal to that of the box ribs, and T-bar diagonals in K pattern at levels of the top and bottom flanges of the boxes. All of the transverse plate girders except those at the portals are lightened by holes in the webs. These transverse beams are designed to resist all of the overturning of the A-frames.

"Portal bracing consists of a transverse built-up haunched beam and T-bar braces to provide a substantial portal with very little loss in

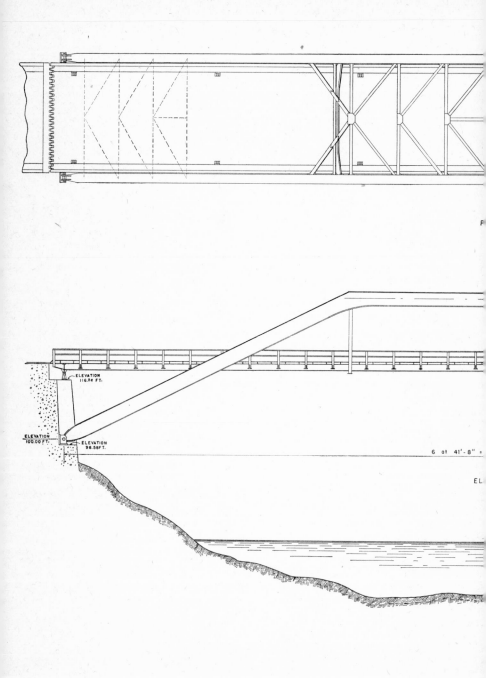

ELEVATION
116.94 FT.

ELEVATION
100.00 FT.

ELEVATION
98.58 FT.

6 at 41'-8" s

EL

Figure 60

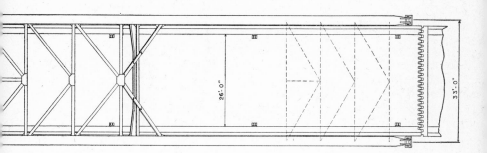

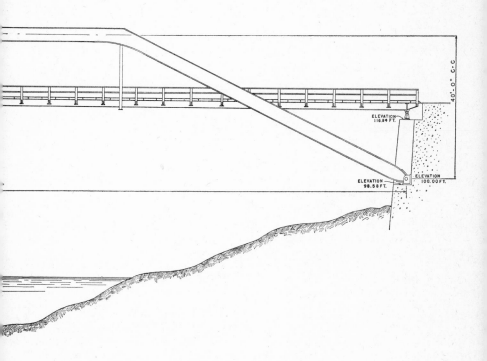

Figure 60 (Concluded)

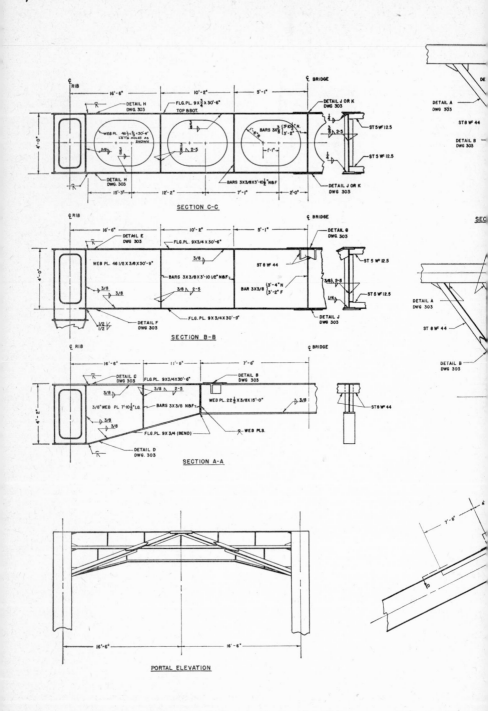

SECTION C-C

SECTION B-B

SECTION A-A

PORTAL ELEVATION

Figure 61

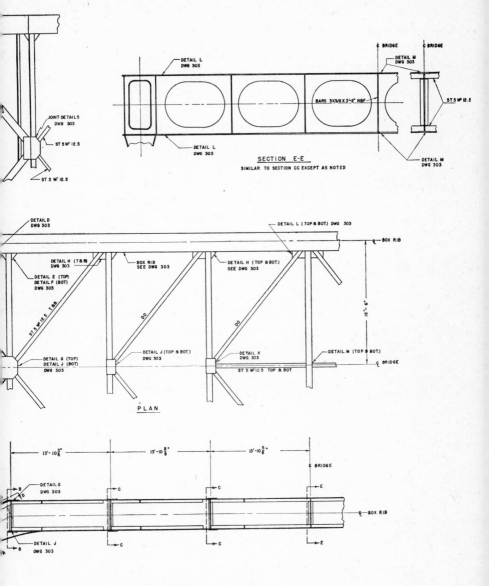

Figure 61 (Concluded)

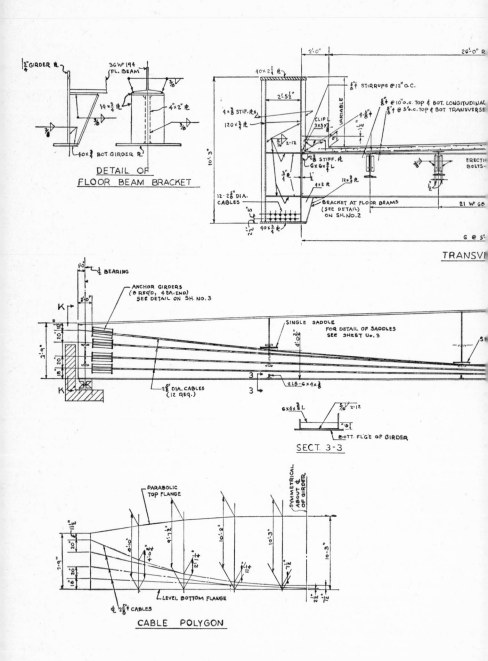

DETAIL OF
FLOOR BEAM BRACKET

SECT. 3-3

CABLE POLYGON

Figure 62

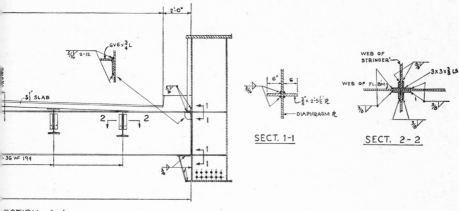

SECT. 1-1

SECT. 2-2

ECTION A-A

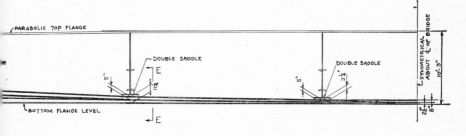

HALF SECTION C-C

HIGH POINTS OF PROJECT FOR A 250 FT.
HIGHWAY BRIDGE ~ H20
COMPOSED OF 2 PRE-STRESSED WELDED
BOX GIRDERS 10'-3"x 2'-6" WITH 40" COV. PLS

THE BOX GIRDERS ARE PRE-COMPRESSED EACH BY 12-2⅝" DIA. GALVANIZED SUSPENSION BRIDGE CABLES STRESSED AT 100,000 P.S.I.

THE CABLE POLYGONS WERE SO CHOSEN THAT FOR DEAD LOAD, THE STRESSES IN EACH BOX GIRDER ARE SUCH THAT IT ACTS LIKE A HORIZONTAL STRUT APPROXIMATING A CENTRALLY LOADED COLUMN. THE PRE-TENSIONED CABLES SLIDING ON SADDLES, IMPART UPWARD FORCES TO THE GIRDERS AT THE POINTS OF SUPPORT, CREATING NEGATIVE MOMENTS AND SHEARS COUNTER BALANCING D.L. MOMENTS AND SHEARS.

UNDER LIVE LOAD A PORTION OF THE ADDITIONAL STRESSES, ABOUT 8% IS TAKEN DIRECTLY BY THE CABLES AND THE REMAINING 92 % PRODUCE L.L. MOMENTS AND SHEARS IN THE GIRDERS WHICH HOWEVER REMAIN IN COMPRESSION TOP AND BOTTOM. THE RATIO L/b OF THE GIRDERS IS 250/3.33= 75.5. DIAPHRAGMS ARE SPACED 27.78' ON CENTER. AN L/b OF 75.5 WILL PRODUCE NO BUCKLING IN THE BOX GIRDER (SEE PAPER BY DR.G.WINTER TRANS. A.S.C.E. VOL. 109, 1944, PP 1336 AND 1359). THE APPORTIONING OF THE LIVE LOAD WAS COMPUTED ACCORDING TO THE ELASTIC THEORY OF STIFFENED SUSPENSION BRIDGES.

THE MAIN GIRDERS AND THE END ANCHOR-AGE GIRDERS WHICH TRANSFER THE CABLE STRESSES TO THE MAIN GIRDERS ARE WELDED BOX GIRDERS.

PRESTRESSING OF THE CABLES IS DONE BY HYDRAULIC JACK BUTTING AGAINST THE END PLATES

Figure 62 (Concluded)

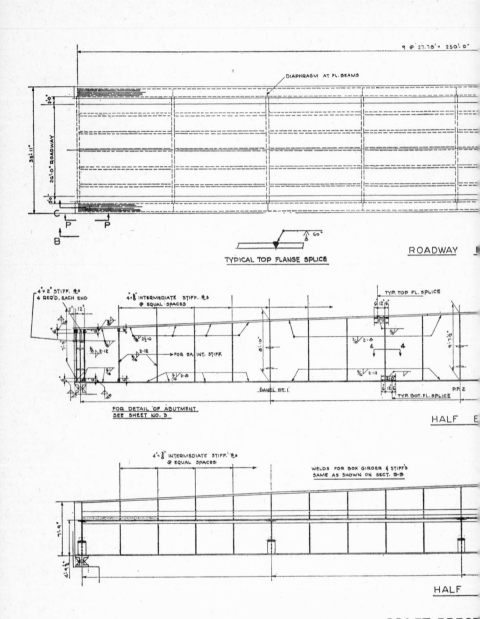

TYPICAL TOP FLANGE SPLICE

ROADWAY

HALF

HALF

250 FT. PRES
PLAN ELEVATIO

Figure 63

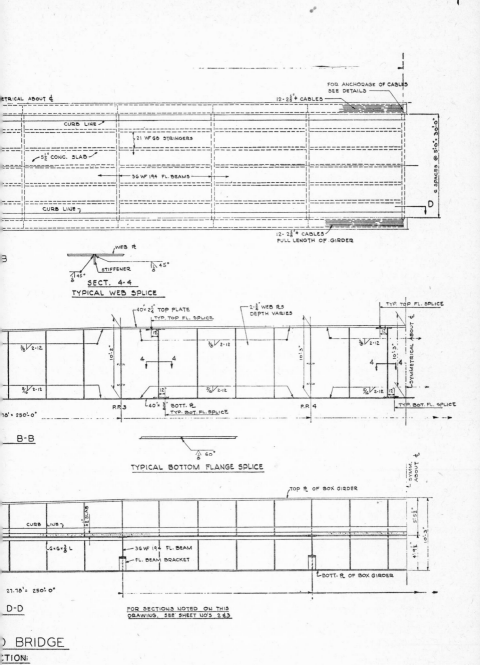

SECT. 4·4
TYPICAL WEB SPLICE

B-B

TYPICAL BOTTOM FLANGE SPLICE

D-D

FOR SECTIONS NOTED ON THIS
DRAWING, SEE SHEET NO'S 2 & 3

BRIDGE

Figure 63 (Concluded)

head room and with artistic proportions. More than the minimum vertical llearance is provided by this design."

Figure 61 shows details of the upper lateral bracing and also the dimensions of the rib of the A-frame. A discussion of the battledeck floor is given in Chapter III.

L. Coff, New York, New York, designed a bridge supported by two box girders each of which contain tensioned cables. A transverse section at the middle of the span is shown in Figure 62. This shows the box girders and the prestressed cables. The box girders have a depth of 10 ft.-3 in. at the center and 7 ft.-9 in. at the ends. The two web plates for each box girder are ¾ in. thick. The top flange is a 40 by 2¼-in. plate and the bottom flange is a 40 by ¾-in. plate. Each box has twelve cables 2⅝ in. in diameter.

The following is a part of Mr. Coff's discussion:

"Prestressing is a structural concept applicable to welded construction, not just to concrete for which it is already being used on a fairly large scale. The principle consists in stressing a structure prior to or simultaneously with loading, so that the resulting stresses are substantially of opposite signs to the ones we expect to arise in the fully loaded structure. This principle has been combined in the present case with the methods used for designing self-anchored suspension bridges. The sag required to make the support by the cables effective is extremely small, because the cables are stressed to capacity at the time they lift the welded steel structure from the false work. Consequently, the part of live load going directly to the cables, and not to the steel girder which functions as a stiffening truss, is extremely small, in our case, about 8 per cent. The importance of such a system is the fact that the cables subdivide the span by the upward reactions they produce at the cable offsets. These latter are provided with saddles like any normal suspension bridge, to equalize the cable stress over the full span. The question whether this construction is justified for spans as small as 250 feet, can be finally answered by comparing the estimate with that of other types of welded construction, and also with prestressed concrete. It is clear, however, that for larger spans, up to 600 feet, the system would compare favorably with other welded construction, because it enables a subdivision of the span by the supporting cables within the box girder.

"There are, however, in this structure, certain technical advantages as to maintenance, probable life, method of erection, and last, but not least, appearance . . . . ."

Figure 62 shows the parabolic top flange and the location of the cables in addition to the transverse section mentioned above. The structural details are shown in Figure 63.

CHAPTER III

FLOOR SYSTEMS

This chapter contains structural details and discussions of some of the floor systems that are designed in the entries of this program. Not all of the entries included complete designs of the floor systems because of the following statements in the Rules and Conditions for the program.

"A floor which serves only as such and does not participate in the strength of the supporting structure shall be designed only so far as is neccessary to indicate the dimensions from which the gross weight is determined. A floor which is designed to contribute to the strength of the supporting structure shall be designed in sufficient detail to indicate the extent and manner of its participation."

For the purpose of definition, a floor system (or floor) includes the floorbeams and all of the structural members supported by the floorbeams. In some designs the floorbeams are unnecessary because the deck or slab is supported by a longitudinal member having transverse brackets. Such longitudinal members are parts of the primary structures which are covered in the preceding chapter.

In addition to the usual floor system composed of a reinforced concrete slab, stringers, and floorbeams, many less common types are used in the bridges of this program. The variation in the floors is considerable. They differ in material, in arrangement and size of members, and in their functions. Some serve as the ties or as stiffening girders for arch bridges. Many are designed so that no other bottom lateral bracing is necessary. The ingenuity of the designers is reflected in the valuable information on floor design which was presented.

The floor systems are divided into three classifications, reinforced concrete, steel grid, and steel plate. A floor having continuous steel plates (or members) covered by concrete is classified as reinforced concrete if the concrete is used structurally, but is classified as steel plate if the concrete serves primarily as a filler and surface material.

Reinforced Concrete

A reinforced concrete floor of some kind was selected by more than half of the participants who designed floor systems. The good roadway surface provided by concrete slabs was the most common reason given for making this selection; however, some concrete slabs are surfaced with an asphaltic material.

A large number of these slabs are reinforced with the conventional steel reinforcing bars and are supported by stringers and floorbeams

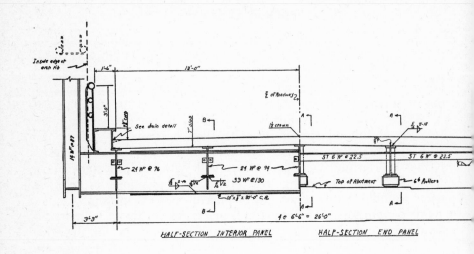

HALF-SECTION INTERIOR PANEL   HALF-SECTION END PANEL

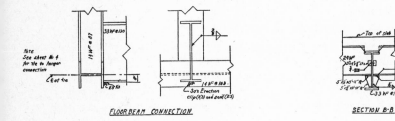

FLOORBEAM CONNECTION   SECTION B-B

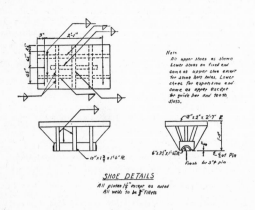

SHOE DETAILS
All plates 1½" except as noted
All welds to be ⅜" fillets

FIXED END

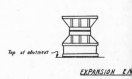

EXPANSION EN

Figure 64

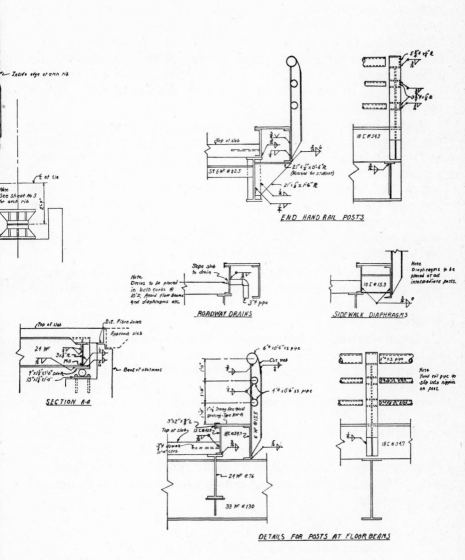

END HAND RAIL POSTS

ROADWAY DRAINS

SIDEWALK DIAPHRAGMS

SECTION A-A

DETAILS FOR POSTS AT FLOOR BEAMS

CURB AND HAND RAIL DETAILS

Figure 64 (Concluded)

in the normal manner. The stringers are continuous in some floors, and in a few of these for arch bridges, the continuous stringers are designed to serve as part of the tie material. In several designs, shear connectors are attached to the stringers or floorbeams (or both) and embedded in the reinforced concrete slab to form composite beams.

Two floors have large stringer spacings and employ two-way slabs. Six designs use precast slab strips, and two of these require the slab strips to be prestressed. A few of the designers utilize folded plates, dished plates, or corrugated sheet as both the forms and a part of the reinforcing for concrete slabs.

Messrs. Bretscher and Briscoe designed a 7-in. reinforced concrete slab for their tied arch which was discussed in Chapter II (see Figures 16, 17, and 18 on pages 52, 54, and 56 respectively). The slab is supported by five 24 WF sections spaced equally at 6 ft.-6 in. center to center. The stringers are supported at the floorbeams (33 WF 130) by seat connections. The floorbeams are positioned and held in place by means of Saxe welded connection units until each end is welded to a hanger and a tie. The details of this floor, including the steel curbing and sidewalk grating, are shown in Figure 64.

In Chapter II, Mr. Rochlin's truss is discussed and two of his drawings are shown as Figure 45 and Figure 46 (pages 116 and 118). The following is his discussion of the floor system he used in this truss bridge:

"The floor stringers are continuous so as to obtain the advantages of continuity. The writer does not regard with too much favor the standard detail generally used here in which the web of the stringer is left unattached to the supporting member. All the details that have come to our attention also show holes punched in either member or both. Another disadvantage of the standard detail is that while the bottom flange of the stringer is bolted to a clip, the upper portion stands free and unbraced. We have in Detail No. 55 and 56 [see Figure 65] made an attempt to solve this problem. In this detail

1. The stringer is supported during construction at both top and bottom.
2. There are no holes in either stringer or floorbeam.
3. Shear is carried directly from web to web.
4. Tolerance is allowed in length of stringer.
5. Some correction may be made in floorbeam distortion as described later.

"The floorbeam connection is also made without the punching of holes. [See Detail No. 58 and 59 of Figure 65.] Here the seat angles are made of bent plates and serve also as seats for the lower chord diagonal bracing.

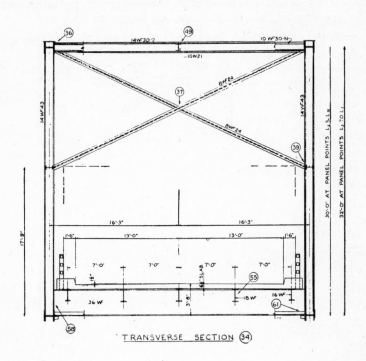

TRANSVERSE SECTION (34)

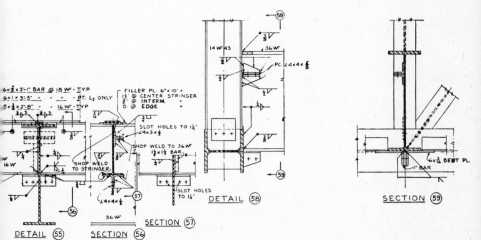

DETAIL (55)   SECTION (56)   SECTION (57)   DETAIL (58)   SECTION (59)

STRINGER CONNECTION DETAILS

Figure 65

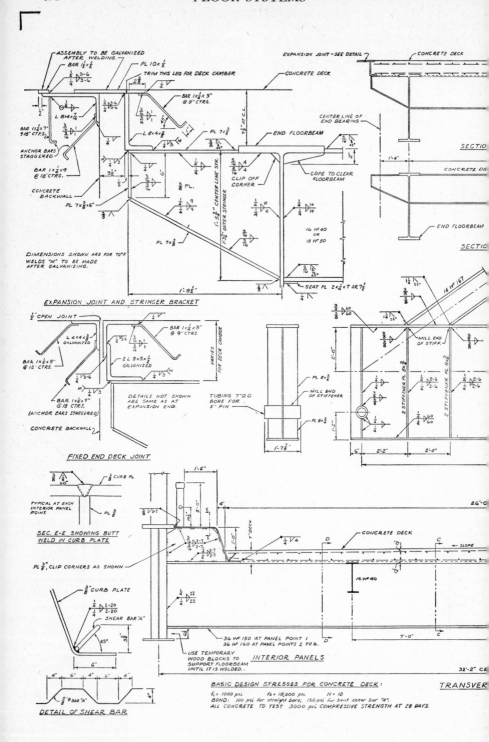

EXPANSION JOINT AND STRINGER BRACKET

FIXED END DECK JOINT

SEC. E-E SHOWING BUTT WELD IN CURB PLATE

DETAIL OF SHEAR BAR

INTERIOR PANELS

BASIC DESIGN STRESSES FOR CONCRETE DECK:
$f_c = 1000$ psi $f_s = 18,000$ psi $N = 10$
BOND: 100 psi for straight bars; 150 psi for bent shear bar "A".
ALL CONCRETE TO TEST 3000 psi COMPRESSIVE STRENGTH AT 28 DAYS.

Figure 66

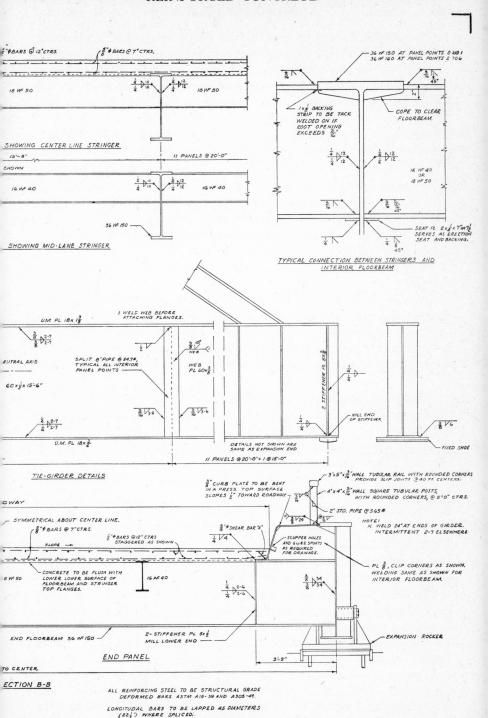

SHOWING CENTER LINE STRINGER

SHOWING MID-LANE STRINGER

TYPICAL CONNECTION BETWEEN STRINGERS AND
INTERIOR FLOORBEAM

TIE-GIRDER DETAILS

END PANEL

SECTION B-B

ALL REINFORCING STEEL TO BE STRUCTURAL GRADE
DEFORMED BARS ASTM A15-39 AND A305-49.

LONGITUDAL BARS TO BE LAPPED 45 DIAMETERS
(22½") WHERE SPLICED.

Figure 66 (Concluded)

"In both the floorbeams and the top lateral struts no end clearance is provided. However, clearance is provided in the bracing diagnosis to make up for any inaccuracy. The usual specification for columns permits a lateral deviation of 1/1000 of the axial length. In 25 ft. this would be a variation of .3 inch. A mechanically guided gas cut will produce a much closer tolerance."

The slab is 6½ in. thick. The interior stringers are 18 WF sections and those at the curbs are 16 WF. The floorbeams are 36 WF sections. The weights of these stringers and floorbeams are given in Figure 45.

Mr. Jennison selected a reinforced concrete slab for the deck of his tied arch (see Figures 1 and 2, pages 14 and 16). Details of this slab and of the stringers and floorbeams are shown in Figure 66. The three stringers are continuous. A curb plate has been designed so that the stringer normally at the curb is omitted.

The following is Mr. Jennison's discussion of the deck and stringer design:

"The deck was designed in reinforced concrete, because this material has the advantages of economy, durability, a desirable traction surface, and gives weather protection for the floorbeams and stringers beneath it. Moreover, the mass and vibration damping qualities of the concrete are desirable from the standpoint of preventing excessive vibration under the action of traffic.

"The lower surface of the deck is made flush with the lower surface of the top flanges of the floorbeams and stringers. By embedding the top flanges of the floorbeams and stringers in the deck in this way, the beams are given adequate lateral support and may be stressed to the full 18,000 p.s.i. basic stress. Moreover, the construction of the deck form is simplified by allowing it to lap under the beam flanges; for the form sheathing need not be cut to fit.

"The main reinforcement of the deck is placed transversely, and longitudinal reinforcing steel is provided for distribution of concentrated loads and to resist temperature stress. For economy and simplicity, all reinforcing steel is straight (without hooks or bends) except one shear bar at each side of the deck.

"To resist lateral forces, the deck is anchored to the curb plate along each edge by shear bars welded to the curb plate. This causes the deck to act as a web and the tie girders as the flanges of a horizontal beam or diaphragm to resist lateral forces. The stresses caused by lateral loads or small.

"Three lines of stringers are provided, and the edges of the deck are supported on the curb plates, which act as edge stringers. The stringers were designed as continuous beams, with welded connections to the floorbeams providing full continuity. The connection detail is simple, but it introduces a stress raiser at the abrupt junction of the top flange of the stringer with the top flange of the floorbeam. Consequently, the design stress was reduced to 75 per cent of the basic 18,000 p.s.i. in accordance with the principle of Art. 229 (c) of the American Welding Society Specifications. This reduction in allowable stress did not increase the weight of the stringers appreciably, because the panel lengths chosen produce negative moments at the supports which are only 78 to 79 per cent of the mid-span positive moments. By using 15-ft. end panels and 20-ft. interior panels, the same stringer sections as are used in the interior panels are adequate in the end panels.

"The end floorbeams are placed 2 ft.-2 in. away from the abutment backwall to make them completely accessible for painting and to simplify the floorbeam connection adjacent to the expansion rocker. This necessitated brackets to support the deck joint assemblies, which serve as edge beams to support the ends of the deck slab. The brackets were designed as simple weldments to extend the three stringers beyond the end floorbeams. The deck joint weldment, brackets, and end floorbeams are to be assembled in the shop and shipped as a single unit. The curb plates extend beyond the deck joint and serve as a support at the ends of the deck joint.

"The connection of the stringer to the floorbeam was designed for ease of erection and welding. The seat plate serves as a temporary support for the stringer and also as backing for the lower flange weld. Backing strips may also be used for the top flange weld whenever the fit-up requires it. Both flanges are welded in the flat position. The web is coped for ample clearance to facilitate placing the stringer on the erection seats. Fillet welds connecting the web of the stringer directly to the web of the floorbeam provide for shear."

Mr. Forster utilizes the six continuous stringers of his floor system as ties for his trussed arches. The horizontal end trusses in the plane of the stringers are proportioned to transmit the stringer forces to the ends of each arch. These stringers (24 WF 76) support an 8¼-in. reinforced concrete slab. They are welded to the tops of the floorbeams (36 WF 150) which are spaced 20 ft.-10 in. center to center.

The horizontal end trusses are designed using flat plates which are reinforced with small webs to improve the slenderness ratio of the members. The webs, however, are not assumed to carry load. Details of these horizontal end trusses and details of other parts of the floor are shown in Figure 67. Information about the arches including Figures 22 and 23 (pages 64 and 66) is given in Chapter II.

A discussion of Mr. Kavanagh's tied arches is presented in the previous chapter where a sectional plan of the grid beams is shown in Figure 3 (page 20) and an end connection of a grid beam in Figure 4

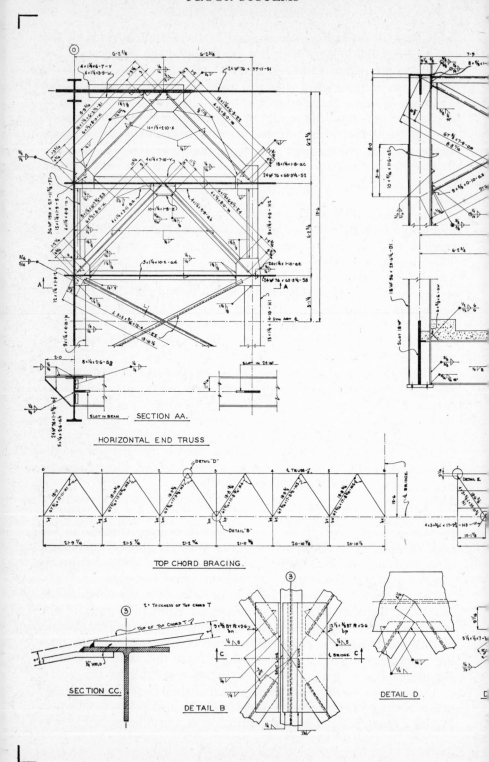

SECTION AA.

HORIZONTAL END TRUSS

TOP CHORD BRACING.

SECTION CC.

DETAIL B

DETAIL D

Figure 67

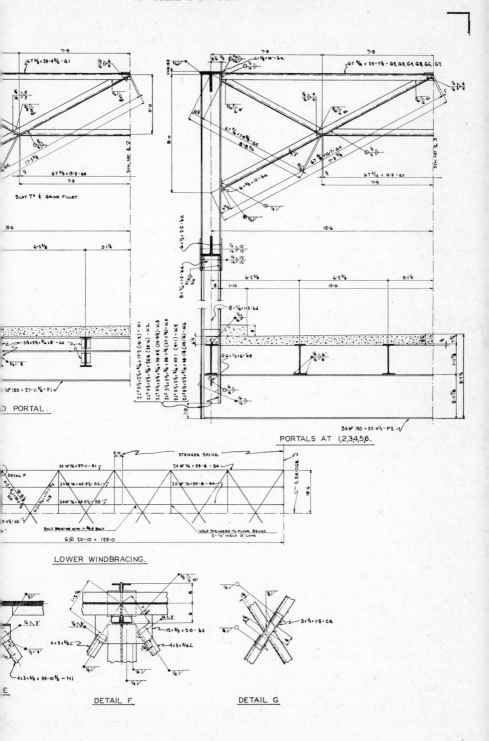

PORTALS AT 1,2,3,4,5,6.

LOWER WINDBRACING.

DETAIL F.

DETAIL G

Figure 67 (Concluded)

(page 22). These grid beams (21 WF 62) are placed diagonally and intersect at their mid-points.

Mr. Kavanagh made the following statements about his floor system:

"The floor system, which also takes the place of the lower lateral bracing, is comprised of a diagonal gridwork of wide-flange beams, each functioning as a composite beam in conjunction with the floor slab. The specific spiral shear connector shown (the alpha system) is included merely for illustration, and may be replaced by any of the other standard systems. No temporary intermediate supports have been assumed during pouring of the slab; if such support is available, the beams could be lightened still further.

"The writer believes that this application of a welded diagonal grid in bridge construction is unique, although the welded diagonal grid has gained considerable recognition and use in a number of industrial structures in Great Britain [see A. H. Pandya and R. J. Fowler, 'The All-Welded Diagonal Grid Applied to Plane and Spatial Structures,' *Arc Welding in Design, Manufacture and Construction,* The James F. Lincoln Arc Welding Foundation, p. 411]. The interaction of a gridwork of beams provides substantial reduction in weight, since all members become beams on elastic supports. This principle has long been recognized. Still, though the use of 'membrances' between beams has been widespread in the United States, the direct utilization in the design calculations of the savings possible in a grid system has generally been avoided because of the apparent complexity of the problem. In Europe, on the other hand, the methods of calculation have been fairly well developed, are recognized in specifications, and are used on many beam and girder bridge designs.

* * *

"The use of this grid floor system works ideally with the arch form adopted, in that it reduces the weight of floor steel required for the widened bridge floor, and at the same time takes the place of the lateral system.

"A study of various possible line loading positions on the roadway indicate that the longitudinal distribution of concentrated loads could be conservatively taken as 50 per cent of the load to the panel point loaded, and 25 per cent to each of the adjacent panel points. This has the important result of reducing the effects of the roving concentrated loadings specified to act in conjunction with uniform lane loadings, and which concentrations are normally placed at the sharp peak of the influence line.

"The floor system allows for the design of the floor slab as a two-way slab, which it is felt is more efficient and more economical than the

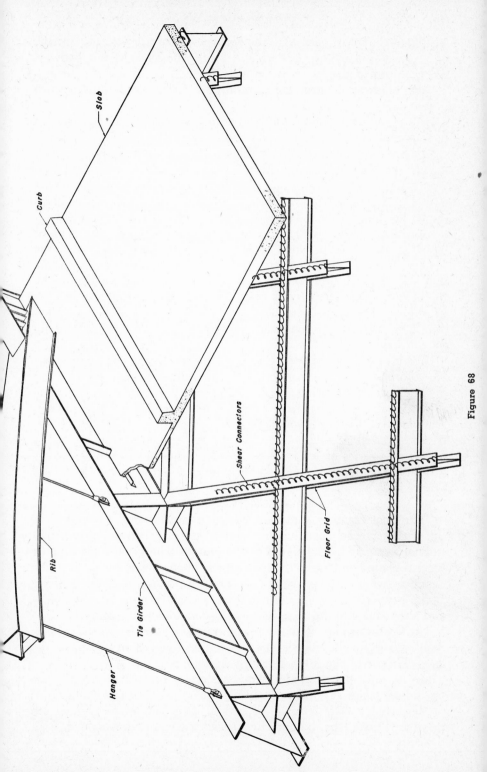

Figure 68

customary one-way slabs. An allowance for concrete wearing surface of a thickness of 1 in. at the curb and 3 in. at the center of the roadway, has been provided.

"The roadway is terminated laterally by a reinforced concrete curb beam. . . ."

Figures 68 and 69 show some additional details of Mr. Kavanagh's floor system.

The floor system used by Mr. Hayes in his tied, three-hinged arch bridge (see Figure 42, page 108) consists of an 8-in. reinforced concrete slab and cross beams spaced 7 ft.-7 in. on centers. There are no stringers. The cross beams are welded directly to the tie members which are box sections. The slab is designed to act structurally with the tie members and with the cross beams—therefore, the top plate of both ties and the top flange of each cross beam is smaller than the bottom plate and bottom flange, respectively. At each cross beam, the slab has a haunch three inches in depth. Anchor hooks welded to the top flange ($6x\frac{3}{8}$) of the cross beam are embedded in the slab in both directions. The cross beams have $19\frac{1}{2}x\frac{3}{8}$-in. webs and $8x1\frac{1}{8}$-in. bottom flange plates. The composite flow serves as bottom lateral bracing for the arches.

Details of Mr. Amirikian's floor are shown in Figure 58 (page 138). He commented on the roadway and floor framing as follows:

"The roadway flooring consists of precast and prestressed concrete panels, measuring 5 ft. wide, 14 ft.-6 in. long and 4 in. thick, which are placed transversely over the stringers. Interconnection of the panels, as well as their connection to the stringers, is provided by means of a series of insert plates cast into the panels and joined by welding. The design contemplates the utilization of a new method of prestressing.

* * *

"The floor framing comprises eleven transverse girders, framed to the trusses at each panel point, and a series of surmounting longitudinal stringers spaced 4 ft.-8 in. on centers. The girders are built of welded plating and have tapering flanges. The stringers consist of 15-in. channels, which are lapped at their ends to provide additional section at the supports; they are connected to each other for full continuity and also welded to the flanges of the girders to act as bracing."

The floorbeams are 36 in. deep, composed of $\frac{1}{2}$-in. webs, 16 by $\frac{3}{4}$-in. flange plates for the middle 11 ft. and 16 by $\frac{5}{8}$-in. flange plates at the ends. These end plates taper to an 8 in. width.

Mr. Freudenthal selected a two-way slab for his bridge (see Figures 55 and 56, pages 134 and 135). In discussing his floor system, he said:

"The bridge floor is made of a 6-in. thick two-way concrete slab reinforced over the bottom by special two-way spot-welded high

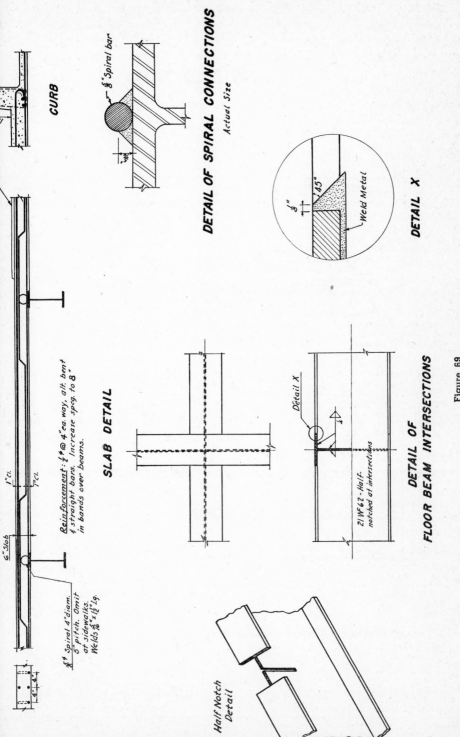

CURB

DETAIL OF SPIRAL CONNECTIONS
Actual Size

⅜" Spiral bar

DETAIL X

Weld Metal

45°

⅛"

SLAB DETAIL

Reinforcement: ½"∅ @ 4" ea. way, alt. bent ½ straight bars. Increase spsg. to 8" in bands over beams.

1" cl.

1" cl.

6" Slab

⅝"∅ Spiral 4" diam. 5" pitch. Omit at sidewalks. Welds ⁵⁄₁₆" x 1½" Lg.

4 4 4

DETAIL OF
FLOOR BEAM INTERSECTIONS

Detail X

21 WF 62 - Half-notched at intersections

Half Notch Detail

Figure 69

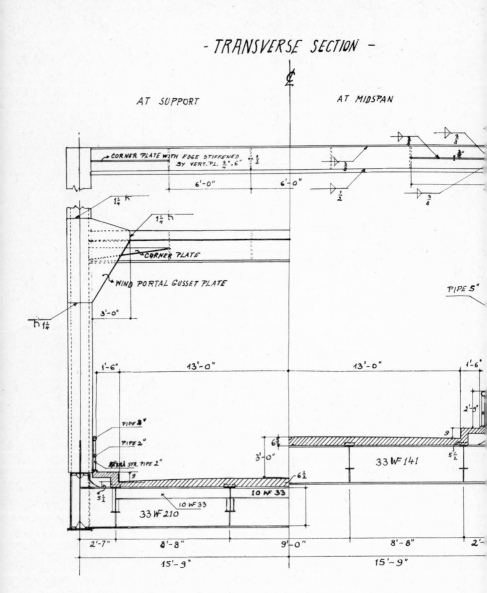

ALL FILLET WELDS $\frac{5}{16}$" UNLESS OTHERWISE NOTED.

Figure 70

DETAILS of FLOOR STRUCTURE

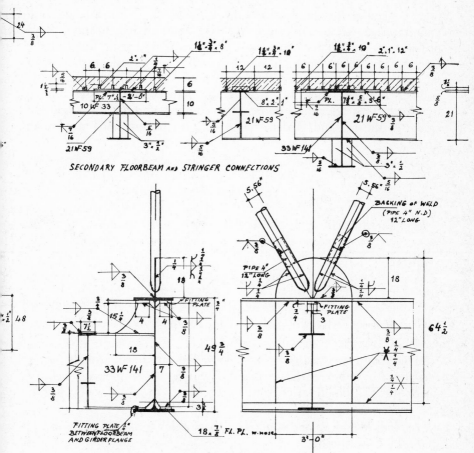

SECONDARY FLOORBEAM AND STRINGER CONNECTIONS

FLOORBEAM AND HANGER CONNECTION TO GIRDER

Figure 70 (Concluded)

strength reinforcing mats, and over the supports by spot-welded strips consisting of reinforcing and distributing bars. The working stresses in the high strength steel mats is 24,000 p.s.i., the compressive design stress in the slab does not exceed 1150 p.s.i., which requires a 3500 p.s.i. concrete. The slab is connected to the secondary floorbeams, the stringers and the main floorbeams by shear keys of variable spacing from 6 in. to 24 in. welded to the top flanges of the beams; thus the combined bending resistance of the steel sections and the concrete slab can be fully utilized in carrying the live load. Since the slab is located practically in the neutral axis of the combined bridge section and is not directly supported on the main girders, the participation of the floor system in the flange stresses is minimized, in accordance with paragraph 225 of the American Welding Society's specifications. This provision is particularly important because of the tensile force in the girders. The relatively high weight of the concrete floor slab is an advantage, since it increases the initial dead load tension forces in the inclined hangers, and thus reduces the compression stresses due to live load. This advantage more than compensates for the slight increase in the rib and girder section due to the increased dead load thrust."

The main floorbeams are 33 WF 141 sections. Two secondary floorbeams (10 WF 53) divide each panel into three equal spans of 9 ft.-0 in. for the end panel and 9 ft.-4 in. for all of the intermediate panels. The four lines of stringers (21 WF 59) provide transverse span lengths for the slab of 8 ft.-8 in., 9 ft.-0 in., and 8 ft.-8 in. Figure 70 shows a transverse section of the bridge and the stringer and floorbeam connections.

Messrs. Daymond and Zakrzewski used a dished plate as the form and the reinforcement for a concrete slab of variable thickness. Figure 71 shows details of this construction (see Figures 36 and 37, pages 94 and 96 for details of the arch). The designers described their floor system as follows:

"The roadway consists of the poured-in-situ hard asphalt carpet reinforced by a No. 12 gauge triangle wire mesh to prevent cracking. Thickness of asphalt varies from 1¼ in. to 1½ in. as shown in Figure 71.

"Asphalt is laid on the concrete slab of thickness varying from 2¾ in. to 6 in. maximum.

"This concrete fills the ¼-in. dished plate. However, its strength is utilized in the design of the deck structure. The concrete nominally reinforced over the supporting stringers and cross girders to prevent cracking, is designed to take compression in the composite slab where steel dished plates take all tension.

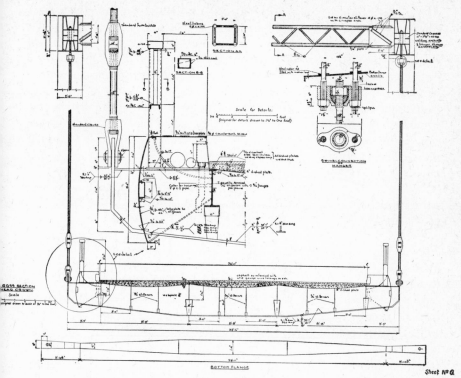

Figure 71

"It is commonly assumed that dished plates act as suspension cables applying a large pull at the points of attachment. The experimental work done by Schaechterle and Leonhardt (see *Bautecknik,* 1938, page 317) proved that provided there is sufficient bond between concrete and steel plate, the latter acts in the same way as ordinary tension reinforcement and can be built quite flat without much pull on the supporting flanges.

"The fact that dished plates are joined by welding enables us to design much more economical sections for the supporting beam. This is shown below.

"To assure bond between concrete and dished plates, the expanded metal mesh is tack welded to the dished plates. A strip of this concrete slab, taken along the stringer and cross girder, also acts as a part of the flange.

"This was assured in this case also by the shear resisting expanded metal.

"That fact enabled the authors to design new rolled unsymmetrical shapes for the stringers. The calculated standard rolled beam for the

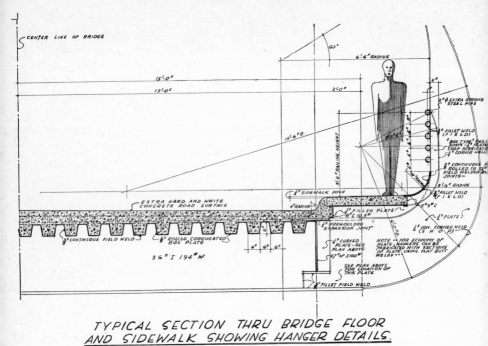

TYPICAL SECTION THRU BRIDGE FLOOR
AND SIDEWALK SHOWING HANGER DETAILS.

Figure 72

same condition is 50 per cent heavier. This is one of the features of the design."

There are four lines of stringers. Each stringer has a top flange 2½ in. wide. The interior stringers are 18 in. deep and have 8-in. bottom flanges. The exterior stringers are 14 in. deep and have 6-in. bottom flanges.

For the floor system of his bridge (see Figures 38 and 39, pages 100 and 102), Mr. Dobert utilized the special deck shown in Figure 72. This deck consists of a ⅜-in. corrugated plate filled with and bonded to a concrete slab that is supported by edge stringers (27 I 160) and floorbeams (36 I 194). The longitudinal stringers are 26 ft. apart. The span of the deck is the 15 ft.-7½ in. between the floorbeams. The plate has box-shape corrugations approximately 6 in. wide and 6 in. deep. The concrete is additionally reinforced with both longitudinal and transverse bars.

Steel Grid

About one-sixth of the floor systems designed have decks of steel grating. Some are open and others are filled with concrete. For all of them, the overall weight is low.

Messrs. Brielmaier and DeLong designed the three-hinged arch shown in Figures 30 and 31 (pages 83 and 84). The floor system for their bridge consists of an open grid flooring, 5-in. I-beam sills, stringers, and floorbeams. The grid is Irving Decking weighing 15.25 lbs. per sq. ft. The sills (5 I 14.75), spaced at 1 ft.-6 in. centers, support the steel deck and in turn rest on stringers (16 WF 50). The authors commented on the design of the stringers and floorbeams as follows:

"The stringers are standard wide-flange rolled sections spaced at 4 ft.-10 in. and designed as beams continuous over five spans of 25 ft., with unyielding supports. The yielding of supports due to differential settlement of the floorbeams would slightly reduce the critical negative moment which governed the size of stringer and would slightly increase the positive moments.

"In order to prevent the stringers from participation in tie-action for the arch, only one bearing on the floorbeams in each 125-ft. length of stringers is fixed. The stringer design also eliminates the possibility of floorbeam distortion due to weld shrinkage, which may occur when the stringers are framed into floorbeams. A traction frame at the two floorbeams with fixed stringer bearings relieves the floorbeams of moment due to longitudinal forces from traffic.

"The transverse floorbeams, spaced at 25 ft. and framing into the stiffening girders, are designed as simply supported beams. The top flanges are considered to receive no lateral support from the stringers and therefore should be larger than the bottom flanges. A welded, built-up beam is used consisting of two special flange sections and a web plate. The end floorbeams are designed to serve as jacking beams if necessary, with plates provided for the jacks."

The details of this floor are shown in Figure 73.

The design of Mr. Percy's trussed arch is described in Chapter II and Figures 19, 20, and 21 show some of the details, including a section of the roadway in Figure 19 (page 60). The floor slab chosen for this bridge is a steel grid (I-Beam Lok Armored Floor Slab) laid with the units transverse to the direction of traffic and filled with concrete. Concerning his floor system, Mr. Percy said:

"The reasons for its choice are many: lightness, strength, long life, economy, and ease and speed of installation.

"The use of the lightweight slabs reduces the dead loads sufficiently to permit a decrease in size of all structural members in the floor system and in the trusses themselves. . . .

"Although the cost of the steel floor system is higher than that of the concrete slab system, the extra cost is more than balanced by a savings in concrete forms and a reduction in steel throughout the bridge. . . .

"The erection of this type of flooring is definitely advantageous.

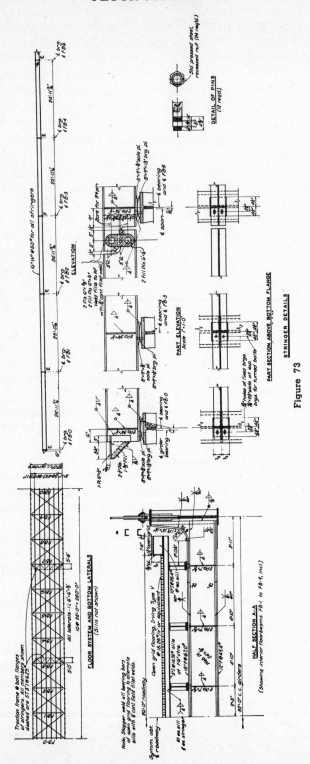

Figure 73

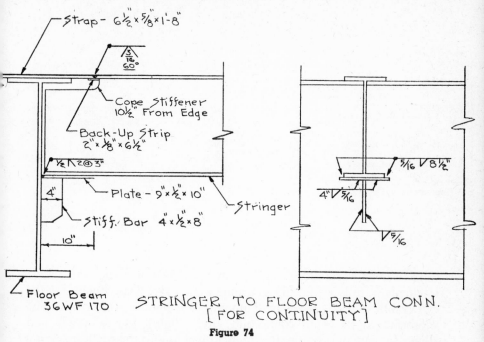

STRINGER TO FLOOR BEAM CONN.
[FOR CONTINUITY]

Figure 74

The flooring units are all cut to proper lengths and widths and reach the job completely shop fabricated. The result is an easy and simple installation. After the units are placed into final positions on top of the upper flanges of the floor stringers, they are welded to them to provide a rigid network of steel at the floor level to resist lateral and longitudinal loads.

* * *

"The floor stringers which support the floor slab were designed to run the length of the bridge. That allowed for a smoother ride for the sag of the floor is parallel to the traffic travel.

"Two kinds of design were considered. First, the stringers were designed to be simply supported at the floorbeams. Then, a continuous condition over 9 spans of 27.77 ft. each was tried. With continuity of stringers it was found that the maximum design moment was reduced 28 per cent, and that the stringer section was 13 lbs. per ft. lighter, with a resultant weight saving of 19.5 kips in dead load weight of stringers alone.

"The type of welded connection between the stringers and floorbeams (Ref: Figure 74) was slightly more difficult to make than for the simply supported case, but was believed to be worth-while from the point of view of weight saved.

"The floorbeams which support the stringers were designed as simply supported beams of constant cross section. At first, the beams

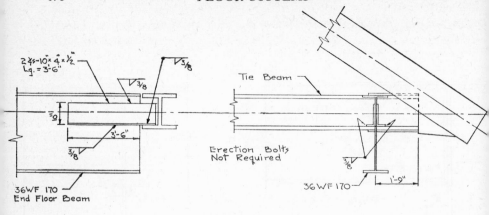

NOTE:- All Floor Beams Connected
To Tie Beam As Shown Above.

END FLOOR BEAM TO TIE BM. CONN

Figure 75

were to be of varying section, having less depth near the ends where moments were low. But, the constant section type was chosen, for the extra fabrication to save a small amount of weight was too costly. The floorbeam to tie beam connection (Ref: Figure 75) is simple and allows for ease of erection, for the field welding to the tie beam is at a minimum and is all in the down position."

Steel Plate.

Many of the floor systems that use steel plates for the roadway decks are designed so that the steel deck will serve as part of the tie or stiffening girder, or both, for the arch bridges and as the bottom lateral bracing in almost every type of bridge. The manner in which the plates are supported and stiffened varies considerably. The different kinds of steel plates include: flat plates with transverse or longitudinal stiffeners, buckle plates filled with asphaltic concrete, corrugated plates filled with concrete, and trussed plates.

Floors having decks of steel plate account for twenty-seven per cent of those floor systems that were designed for this program.

Mr. Amstutz designed a floor system that is so much an integral part of the primary structure that it was discussed with the arch in Chapter II. It is a corrugated plate (filled with concrete) that is supported by a single longitudinal girder of semi-circular shape located at the centerline of the roadway and having floorbeams similar to cantilever brackets.

This unusual floor is shown in Figures 26 and 27 on pages 74 and 76.

The tied arch designed by Mr. Seegers is described in Chapter II. He uses the steel roadway as the tie for the arch and also as bottom lateral bracing as indicated by the details in Figure 76. His desire to have continuity in structures is evidenced in his discussion as follows:

"By welding, various individual steel shapes are molded into one monolithic construction. The design of welded bridges and of all welded constructions ought to be based hereon. The calculation of such a bridge must assume that all parts act together, i.e., that there are no individually regarded members as stringers, cross girders, etc. The author believes that—in spite of some difficulties in calculation— this method of design will help to develop economic welded bridges which are free from relationship to riveted constructions. There are already some deck bridges built according to this idea."

The roadway plate is stiffened on a transverse direction at the cross girders and in longitudinal direction by the stiffening ribs that are 8 in. deep and spaced slightly more than one foot apart. These stiffened plates are to be fabricated in long units and in widths so that 3 units will cover the transverse distance between the curbs. These units will be placed on two longitudinal girders and on cross girders and welded to them. The horizontal plate distributes the loads over the longitudinal stiffening ribs. These ribs and the horizontal plate distribute loads over the cross girders. The 9/16-in. plate serves as the top flanges for the ribs and also for the cross girders.

All of the longitudinal material including the horizontal plate, ribs, longitudinal girders, and the steel curbs are taken into account for the tie and in calculating the longitudinal stiffness of the roadway construction which acts together with the arch ribs in taking moments and shearing forces.

The hanger spacing is 20 ft.-10 in., but the distance between cross girders is 10 ft.-5 in., except for the end panels that are divided into 3 rather than 2 spans.

Mr. Mulder used his steel roadway as a tie for his arch bridge (see Figures 32, 33, and 34 starting on page 86). As shown in Figure 77, this steel plate increases in width in the end panels for the connection to the arch ribs. At the ends, the checkered plate is ½ in. thick; between the ends, it is 7/16 in. thick. For the entire length and width of the roadway, the checkered roadway plate is covered with a rubber-asphalt coating. The reasons given for selecting a steel plate with a special coating were:

"A concrete bridge-road has been avoided on account of its weight and cost, but allowing traffic to pass directly on the steel plate has the following disadvantages.

1. The plate becomes very slippery in the long run, even if the plate should have been made uneven and rough.

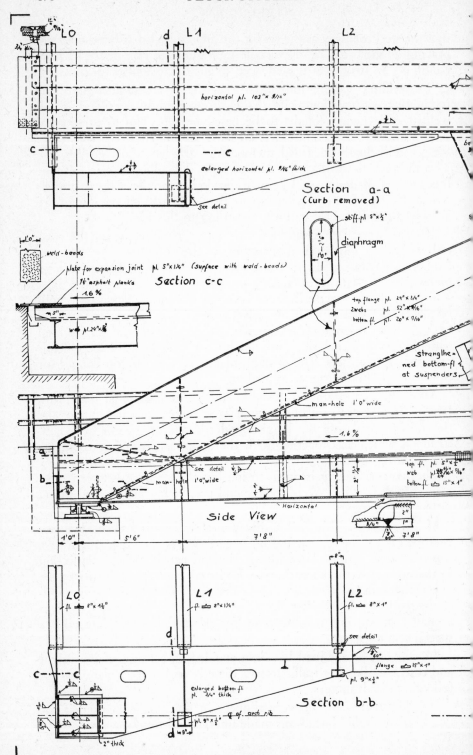

Figure 76

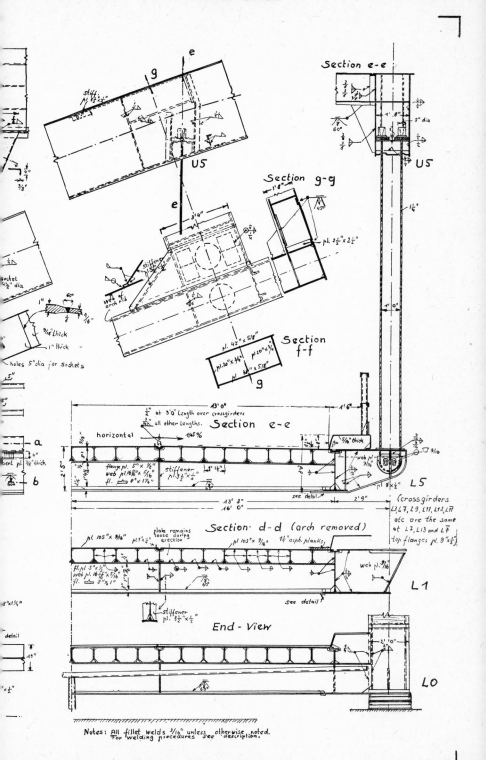

Figure 76 (Concluded)

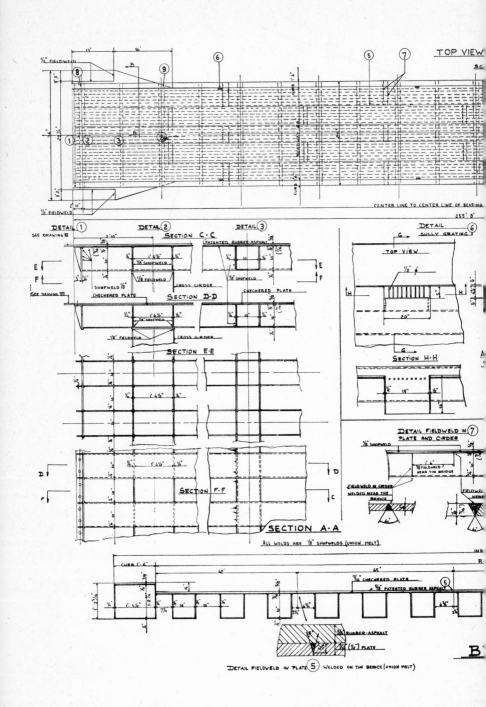

Figure 77

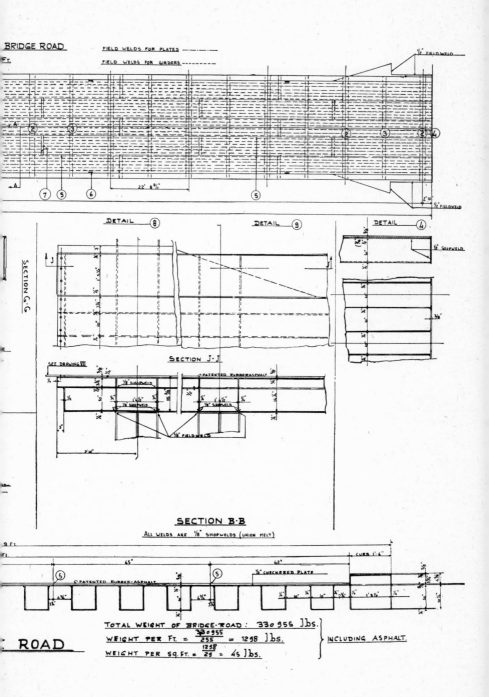

Figure 77 (Concluded)

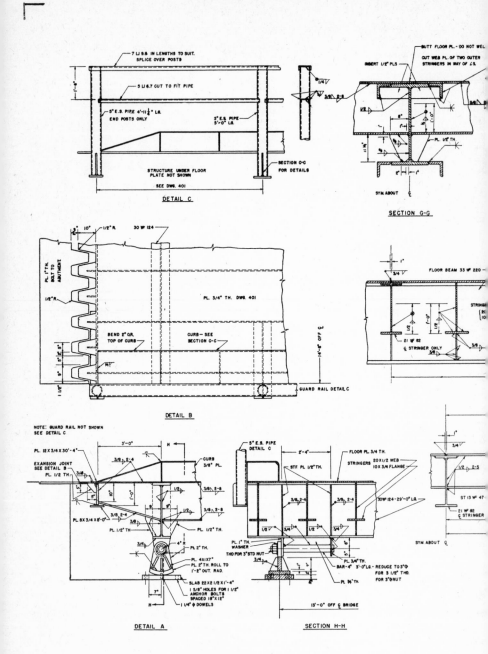

Figure 78

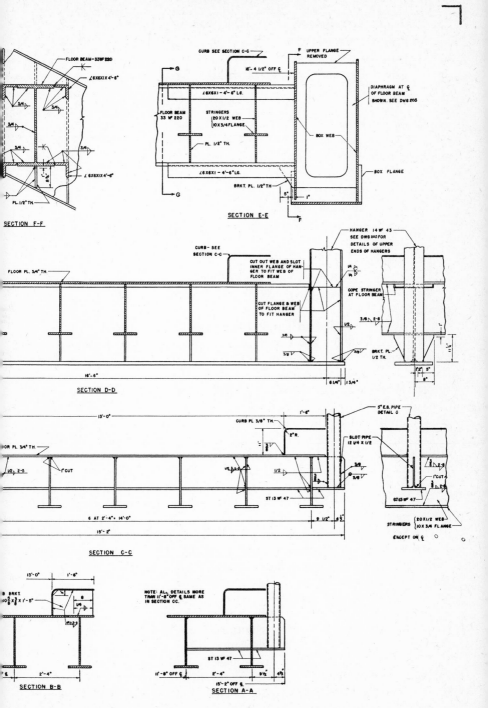

Figure 78 (Concluded)

2. The dirt of the rust is very troublesome and the rumble of the traffic is not softened.

3. Rustproof steel is too expensive to be applied.

4. The bridge-plate will not be flat after welding.

"Therefore we cover the steel plate with a rubber-asphalt coating of a thickness of ⅜ in. This kind of coating has been patented in my country.

"The firm which puts this rubber-asphalt on the market has an experience of fifteen years and guarantees the following properties of it.

1. No stripping up, not even with the heaviest traffic and not even at a temperature of about 50 degrees C.

2. It adheres to the steel in an exceptionally firm way and it does not crack.

3. Absolutely skid-proof and deadens sound.

4. A new coating can be placed on an old one without more ado.

"Before the rubber-asphalt coating is fixed, the steel plate must be sand-blasted."

The plate is welded to longitudinal channels of special shape—10 in. by 10 in. with thickness of ¼ in. The channels are spaced with a clear distance between them of 10 in. (see Figure 77). This plate and channel combination becomes a longitudinal unit that is supported at the panel points by floorbeams of box shape, 1 ft.-6 in. wide and 4 ft.-6 in. deep. Midway between panel points, transverse diaphragms form cross members that distribute applied loads in a transverse direction.

The design of Messrs. Waling, Lawton, Lewiecki, Pyke, and Radcliffe is discussed in Chapter II where two of the drawings are shown is Figures 60 and 61 (pages 144 and 146). For this bridge, there are 6 panels and the distance between floorbeams is 41 ft.-8 in. The end floorbeams are 30 WF 124 sections; the interior floorbeams are 33 WF 200 sections.

The floor plate is welded to the top edge of the web of tees to form a plate-stringer combination that is supported by the floorbeams. The plate is ¾ in. in thickness. The tees are spaced at 2 ft.-4 in. centers. Each tee consists of a 20 by ½-in. web and a 10 by ¾-in. bottom flange. As shown in Figure 78, a series of transverse tees (ST 13 WF 47) are welded between the webs of the longitudinal tees to provide transverse stiffness for load distribution. There are five series of these transverse tees between each floorbeam.

These plate-stringer units are equal in width to one-half of the roadway and are welded together in the field along the centerline of the roadway. A 21 WF 82 stringer is located at the roadway centerline in order that this field weld may be made directly above its top flange.

The authors stated, "While the road surface is not an essential part of this exhibit, the design is based on the use of asphalt plank surface as described on page 4 of 'The Bottledeck Floor for Highway Bridges' by A.I.S.C. (1938)."

Mr. Akroyd's bridge is discussed in Chapter II, and reference there (see page 49) is made to Figure 79 and 80 which are included here to show details of his unusual floor system. The two cross sections in Figure 79 indicates how the new tees (9x2 at 3.75 lb. per ft.) are supported by cross girders spaced every 6 ft.-3 in. These tees have bottom flanges 9 in. wide and webs that extend 2 in. above the top of the flange. The tees are 50 ft. long and are welded at the ends for continuity. Concrete is poured to a level equal to the top of the webs to provide an even road surface.

The cross beams are fabricated as shown in Figure 80. The web of a rolled beam is serrated in a longitudinal direction. The pieces are moved so that the extreme edges of the web are in contact. Then, the webs are welded together along the contact surfaces. Mr. Akroyd said: "Broad Flange Beams castellated—i. e. cut and rewelded in the web (British Patent Rights No. 498281)." This process produces a beam of greater depth and stiffness with a web having regularly spaced holes. The depth is increased from 18 in. to 24 in.

The cross beams frame into stiffening girders that are composed of tee flanges (a new section 24 x 6) and a web, 24x¾ in. The stiffening girders are supported at the hangers every 25 ft. These girders serve as the ties for the arch.

This construction eliminates the need of stringers and bottom lateral bracing.

Mr. Malkiel designed the two-hinged arch shown in Figure 10 (page 38). The floor system, called a "Roadway Plate," acts as the tie and the stiffening member for the arches. It is a "space trussed and stiffened floor plate, capable of transmitting shear and bending in any direction." The primary element is "the floor plate itself that serves simultaneously as a roadway surface, structural stem of the entire roadway system, and a horizontal tie between the arches." Figure 11 (page 40) shows in Detail K how the width of the plate increases at the ends of the span for the connection to the arches.

Mr. Malkiel said: "The Roadway Plate consists of six prefabricated units. By the interlocking of these units with a longitudinal weld, in the field, as shown in Detail E of Figure 12 (page 42) and providing transverse bottom chords at the hanger points (this portion called hereafter Transverse Bent as shown on Section DD of Figure 10) all six units will act as one rigid Roadway Plate.

The floor plate is top flange material for both the longitudinal

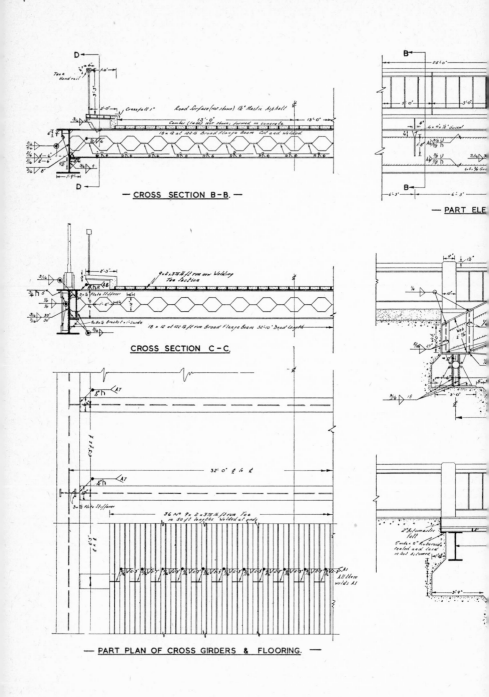

— CROSS SECTION B–B. —

CROSS SECTION C–C.

— PART PLAN OF CROSS GIRDERS & FLOORING. —

— PART ELE

Figure 79

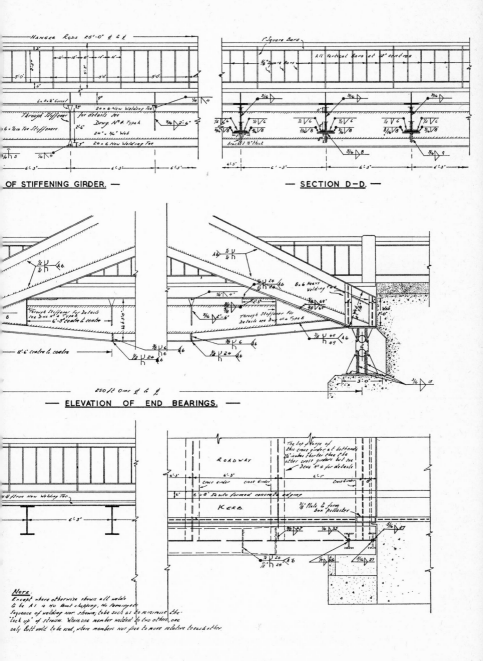

— OF STIFFENING GIRDER. —   — SECTION D-D. —

— ELEVATION OF END BEARINGS. —

Note.
Except where otherwise shown all welds
to be A1 in No Boat chipping, no swing to
sequence of welding nor shown, to be such as to minimise the
'lock up' of stress. Where one member welded to two others, one
only butt weld to be used, where members not free to move relative to each other.

Figure 79 (Concluded)

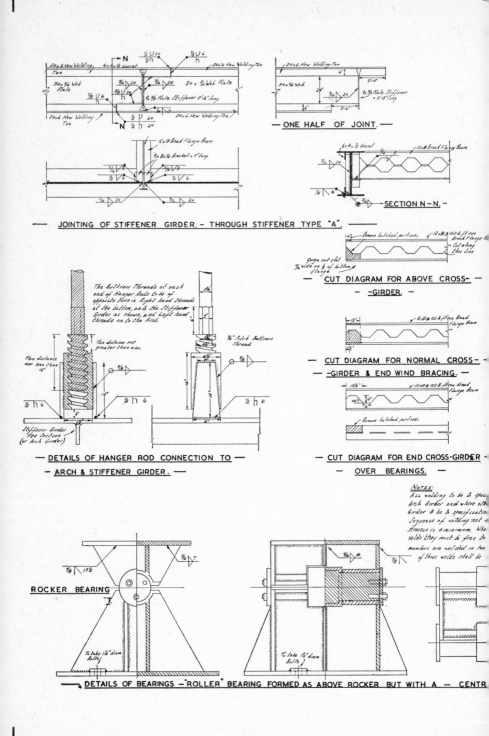

— JOINTING OF STIFFENER GIRDER. – THROUGH STIFFENER TYPE "A". —

— ONE HALF OF JOINT. —

— SECTION N–N. —

— CUT DIAGRAM FOR ABOVE CROSS– –GIRDER. —

— CUT DIAGRAM FOR NORMAL CROSS– –GIRDER & END WIND BRACING. —

— CUT DIAGRAM FOR END CROSS-GIRDER OVER BEARINGS. —

— DETAILS OF HANGER ROD CONNECTION TO — ARCH & STIFFENER GIRDER. —

ROCKER BEARING

— DETAILS OF BEARINGS –"ROLLER" BEARING FORMED AS ABOVE ROCKER BUT WITH A — CENTR

Figure 80

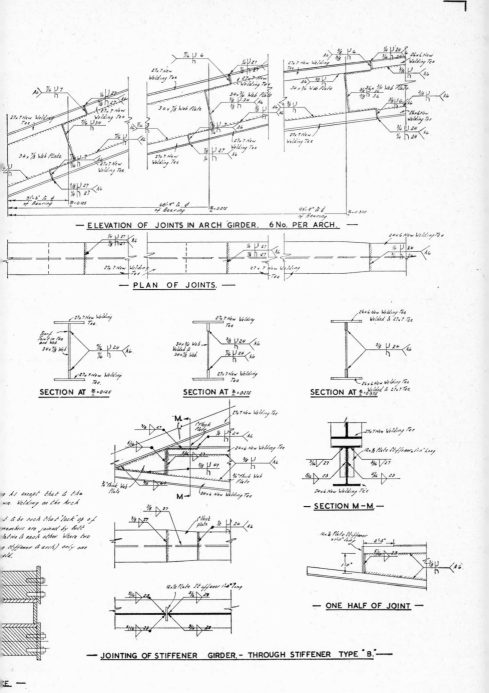

— ELEVATION OF JOINTS IN ARCH GIRDER. 6 No. PER ARCH. —

— PLAN OF JOINTS. —

SECTION AT ℥ = 0·125

SECTION AT ℥ = 0·275

SECTION AT ℥ = 0·375

M—

M—

— SECTION M—M. —

— ONE HALF OF JOINT —

— JOINTING OF STIFFENER GIRDER,— THROUGH STIFFENER TYPE "B." —

Figure 80 (Concluded)

STIFFEN

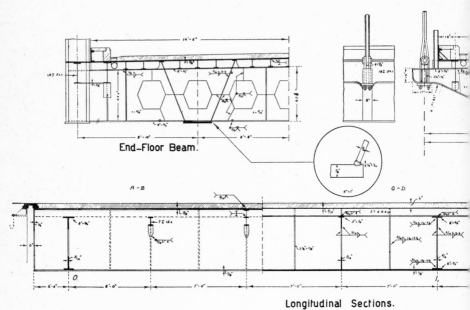

End-Floor Beam.

Longitudinal Sections.

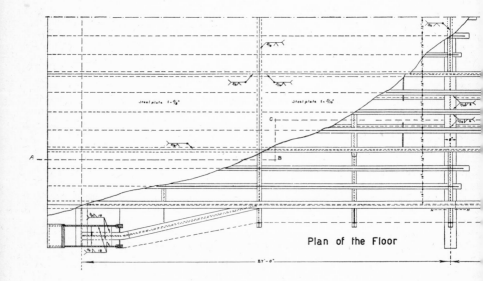

Plan of the Floor

Figure 81

BEAMS AND FLOOR.

drawing of details.

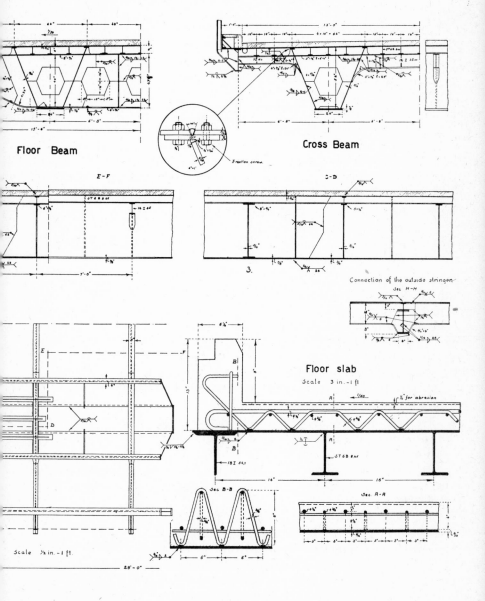

Floor Beam

Cross Beam

Floor slab
Scale 3 in. - 1 ft

Connection of the outside stringer

Figure 81 (Concluded)

trusses (Unit Plate) and the transverse trusses (Transverse Bent). The floor plate is a series of channels with inclined edges that are welded together in the field. Both the longitudinal and transverse trusses have special bottom flanges and space diagonals.

According to the author, his design was guided by the following general outline:

1. Create a universal prefabricated unit product for bridge structure by means of the most efficient use of modern welding technique.

2. Use of efficient multiplication of typical parts required for assembly of the prefabricated nuclear unit—thus making full use of the modern facilities of a welding shop.

3. An efficient arrangement of stressed members. Basically to be accomplished by replacement of 'monaxial' stressed members (such as prevailing in conventional systems of girder, floorbeam and stringer grids) to 'biaxial' stressed members, which are capable of being stressed in, or to receive loads from, two principal directions or subsequently any direction.

4. Reducing the dead weight of the structure to a minimum by employing all metals that comprise the structure as stressed, structural members.

For the arch bridge submitted by Messrs. Gorgolewski and Lecewicz, the floor system functions as an important part of the primary structure. As mentioned in Chapter II and shown in Figure 5 (page 26), the stiffening girders are located inward from the arches in a position to support the floor. Collectively, the stiffening girders and the floor plate stiffened by longitudinal tees act both as a tie and stiffening member for the two-hinged arches. The horizontal thrust from both arch ribs is distributed by suitable horizontal girders at the ends of the span to the entire cross section of the floor system.

The economics of this type of construction are given with a discussion of the stiffening girder in Chapter II. Figure 81 gives the details of the members of the floor system. The two trapezoidal girders are spaced 13 ft.-4 in. between centers. Each one is 24 in. wide at the bottom, 64 in. wide at the top, and 52 in. deep. The floor plate is used as the top flange.

The floor plate is 5/16 in. thick except in the end panels where it is ⅝ in. thick. The plate in the end panel serves as a web for the horizontal girder that transfers the arch thrust to the floor system. The end floorbeam and the first interior floorbeam act as the flanges of the horizontal girder. The plate is stiffened throughout the entire length of the bridge by tees, 6 in. deep, that are spaced 16 in. between centers. The plate is covered with 4 in. of reinforced concrete. Some of the transverse reinforcing steel is welded to the plate to insure composite action. This type of floor makes other bottom lateral bracing unnecessary.

The details of the floorbeams and cross beams are shown in Figure 81. There are three cross beams per panel; that is, one every 7 ft. except for the end panels. Floorbeams are located at the panel points. The end panels are 27 ft. long; the interior panels are 28 ft. long.

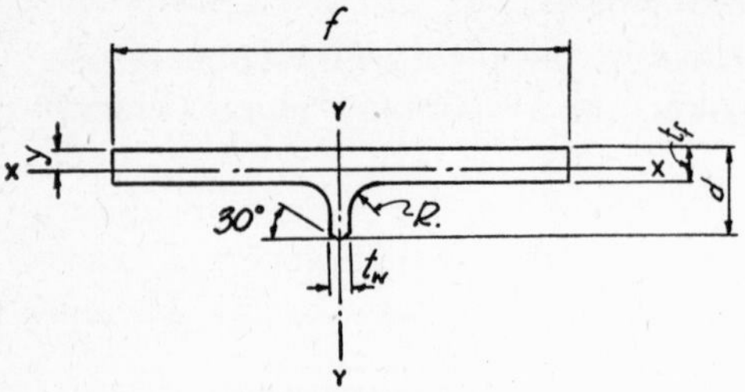

"F" SECTIONS 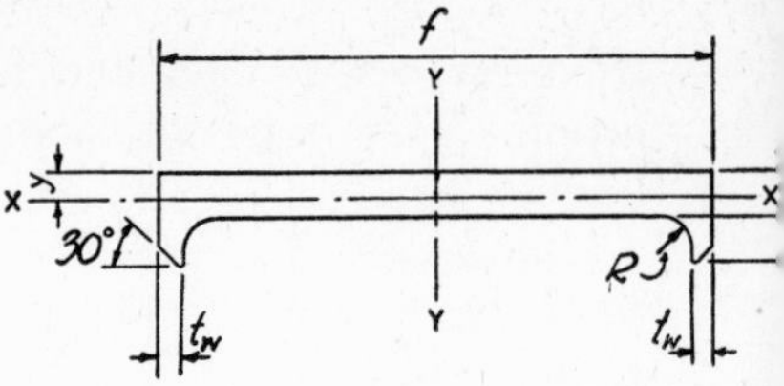   "C" SECTIONS

PROPERTIES OF SPECIAL SECTIONS											
Section Number	Weight per Foot	Area	Radius (R.)	Depth (d)	Flange		Stem Thickness (tw)	Axis X-X			Axis Y-Y	
					Width (f)	Thickness (tf)		I	r	y	I	r
	lb.	in.²	in.	in.	in.	in.	in.	in.⁴	in.	in.	in⁴	in.
12"F	49.4	14.54	.80	2.50	12.00	1.125	.750	3.08	.460	.651	162	3.34
15"F	67.0	19.69	.90	2.50	15.00	1.250	.750	3.96	.448	.685	352	4.23
16"F	65.2	19.18	.90	3.00	16.00	1.125	.625	4.75	.498	.654	384	4.48
16"C	73.3	21.56	.90	2.50	16.00	1.250	.625	5.05	.486	.716	521	4.92

Figure 82

CHAPTER IV

NEW SECTIONS

The selection of steel shapes for the members of the bridges presented in this program was not limited to those in production at the time. In fact, the Rules and Conditions stated: "the participants are encouraged to incorporate sections in their design that are not now available provided the design can be improved thereby. The only limitation in this regard is that the new sections specified must be of such shape that they can be readily produced if a sufficient demand develops." Not all of the new sections proposed could be produced with the rolls and dies presently in use. For a few of the new shapes, additional rolls or dyes would be required.

The previous chapters have contained a little information about some of the new sections in the discussion of the designs, but such information was of secondary importance there. Here it is of primary importance, and the entire chapter is devoted to the details and advantages of the new shapes. For easier comparison, the sections are grouped with others of similar shape. Although all of the new sections are not discussed here, the intention has been to include one or more of every type proposed.

Most of the shapes may be classified as special plates, tees, beams, channels, or angles. A few unusual sections are covered in a miscellaneous group. Circular pipes or tubes are not included even though some new sizes were proposed. Sections having a uniform curvature are discussed under plates.

Plates

Many designers suggested plates with special edges, bulb ends, ribs, varying thickness, or a combination of these. The modified plates of this group represent some of the proposed sections that deviate from the common rectangular plate.

Messrs. Brielmaier and DeLong have special flange sections on their floorbeams (see Figure 73, page 174). The tie girder has similar flange sections (see Figure 31, page 84). The top member of the arch is also a special section. It could be considered a new channel, or a plate with special turned edges. The dimensions of these new shapes are given in Figure 82.

The authors said: "Figure 82 shows the section, dimensions, and properties of four sections which are not rolled at this time. Three of these are flange sections for single-web, built-up members and have a shape resembling a tee with a greatly stunted stem. The fourth is a flange section for double-web, built-up members and has a channel shape.

"All of these new sections have the advantage of moving the flange-to-web welds away from the face of the flange, resulting in better stress conditions and facilitating the welding operation and the examination of welds by X-rays.

"It would be highly desirable to have a series of each of the types of flange sections here discussed, rolled as a standard section. The exact dimensions and properties should be the subject of careful study from the viewpoint of possible use in various ranges of girders and truss design."

Mr. Freudenthal used a special plate with a "shallow nose" as the bottom flange of his stiffening girder (bottom chord). This plate is shown in Figure 83. It is a plate that has a special stem or stub. The top of the stem is beveled for welding.

In discussing the value of this section, Mr. Freudenthal said:

"With regard to specific details of the design of the stiffening girder it was considered particularly important to avoid in the vicinity of the highly stressed fibers all fillet welds perpendicular to the direction of the principal tensile stresses. Therefore, the web stiffeners are not welded to the girder flanges, but are supported against them by closely fitting small plates welded only to the stiffeners. While such an arrangement is usually found in the bottom flanges of welded bridge girders, the existence of an axial tension force and the moment reversal due to live load makes such arrangement here desirable in both flanges, although resulting tensile stresses in the top flange are, in general, considerably smaller than in the bottom flange. Because of this difference in the intensity of the tensile stresses in the top and bottom flanges the use of a special plate profile and with a shallow nose, as indicated in Figure 56 (page 135) or Figure 83, is proposed for the bottom flange only; the more lightly stressed top flange which must moreover be slotted at the hangar connections is made of standard plate. In this manner at least the most critical fillet welds in the structure are replaced by longitudinal butt welds between the bottom flange and the web. It has been the general experience that whenever a crack occurred in a welded web girder, it invariably originated in the fillet-welded joint between the standard plate of the tension flange and the web. Therefore, in practically all countries in which bridge welding has made rapid progress, special plates with shallow noses for use as flanges of welded web girders are being rolled. The use, for this purpose, of structural tees cut from wide flange sections is an inadequate and uneconomical substitute, particularly because of the thick stem in relation to the width of the section. . . ."

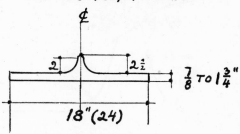

SPECIAL NOSE-PLATE
FOR BOTTOM FLANGE

Figure 83

Mr. Seegers used bulb flats and special plates with welding stems in his design. The plate with a flange, or bulb, on one end is utilized as the longitudinal stiffeners for the roadway plate (see Figure 76, page 178). A special plate with a welding stem is shown with the bulb plate in Figure 84. This plate is the bottom flange of the cross girder.

Mr. Seegers stated: "The longitudinal ribs of the horizontal plate are of a section generally not used in bridge building. Bulb-flats as they are known in shipbuilding may be convenient and will be easily obtainable. Figure 84 shows dimensions proposed.

"The proposed bottom flange for cross girders has the advantage that it may be joined to the web by one butt weld. This weld is not situated at regions of maximum stress. It is known that sections with welds directly at the flange resulted in failures.

"The same type of section is proposed for the bottom flange of the longitudinal girder.

"It is proposed to roll such sections in widths of 8, 10, 12, 15, 18, 21, and 24 in. The thickness may vary by ⅛-in. increments to meet various requirements. The minimum thickness may be ½ in. for 8-in. and 1¼ in. for 24-in. width. The nose is 2 in. high in all sections. It has sufficient thickness to weld webs up to ¾ in. to the flange. The form of the nose may be the same for all widths above mentioned."

Although Mr. Amstutz did not suggest that plates be rolled to the shape of his curved and folded plates shown in Figure 27 (page 76), he made good use of these sections formed from regular flat plates. The folded plate is the primary part of the roadway deck, and the curved plate constitutes the single longitudinal girder located at the centerline of the bridge.

The folded plate is trapezoidal in shape. It has a thickness of ⅜ in., a depth of 4 in., and a distance of 12 in. between centerlines of troughs.

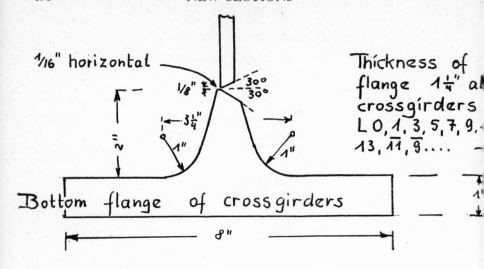

1/16" horizontal

1/8"

3¼"

1"

1"

30°
30°

Thickness of flange 1¼" at crossgirders L 0, 1, 3, 5, 7, 9, 13, 11, 9 ....

Bottom flange of crossgirders

8"

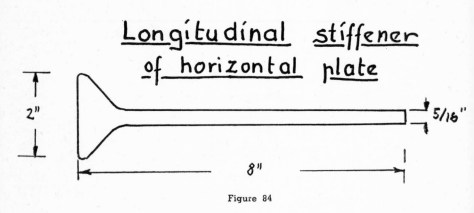

Longitudinal stiffener of horizontal plate

2"

5/16"

8"

Figure 84

The curved plate has a radius of 5 ft. and is ⅜ in or ⁷⁄₁₆ in. thick, depending on its spanwise location.

M. J. Volsing, Hedehusene, Denmark, suggested the new shapes shown in Figure 85 in the design of his tied arch. These are called CW, IW, EW, and YW sections. The CW30 section is used in the rigid member for the arch rib which is composed of four CW30 sections, one 20 x ⁷⁄₁₆-in. plate, and sixteen 1-in. round bars. The IW16 sections are stringers, and the EW and YW sections are the flanges of the floorbeams.

In Mr. Volsing's words: "CW sections are bent plates of uniform thickness so they conveniently can be butt-welded together end to end. Whether the rounded corners of these sections improve the appearance of the structure is of course a matter of taste.

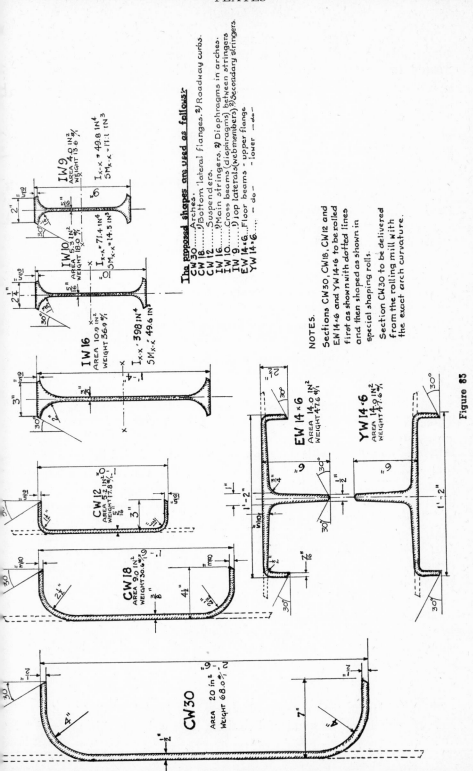

IW9
AREA 4.0 IN²
WEIGHT 13.6 #/
$I_{x-x} = 49.8$ IN⁴
$5M_{x-x} = 11.1$ IN³

IW10
AREA 5.3 IN²
WEIGHT 18.0 #/
$I_{x-x} = 71.4$ IN⁴
$5M_{x-x} = 14.5$ IN³

IW16
AREA 10.9 IN²
WEIGHT 36.9 #/
$I_{x-x} = 398$ IN⁴
$5M_{x-x} = 49.6$ IN³

CW12
AREA 5.2 IN²
WEIGHT 17.8 #/

CW18
AREA 9.0 IN²
WEIGHT 30.6 #/

CW30
AREA 20 in²
WEIGHT 68.0 #/

EW 14 × 6
AREA 14.0 IN²
WEIGHT 47.6 #/

YW 14·6
AREA 14.9 IN²
WEIGHT 47.6 #/

The proposed shapes are used as follows:

CW 30......Arches.
CW 18......}Bottom lateral flanges. 2) Roadway curbs.
CW 12......Suspenders.
IW 16......}Main stringers. 2) Diaphragms in arches.
IW 10......}Cross beams (diaphragms) between stringers
IW 9......} Top laterals(web members)2)Secondary stringers
EW 14·6..Floor beams - upper flange
YW 14·6.... — do — - lower — do —

NOTES.

Sections CW30, CW18, CW12 and
EW 14·6 and YW 14·6 to be rolled
first as shown with dotted lines
and then shaped as shown in
special shaping rolls.

Section CW30 to be delivered
from the rolling mill with
the exact arch curvature.

Figure 85

"IW sections. Where a greater moment of inertia about the web is not required, these IW sections are probably more convenient for maintenance and also for welding to other shapes than ordinary I sections. Deformations due to rolling operations are smaller than for standard I beams.

"EW and YW sections. These are primarily intended to be girder flanges with the following advantages: They have a rather high moment of inertia about the stem axis. Flange plates can be added without altering outside appearance or the total height of the girder."

Figure 72 (page 172) shows a typical section through the floor of Mr. Dobert's bridge. A ⅜-in. plate has been used as a form and also as a part of the tensile reinforcement for the concrete slab. The depth is 6 in. and the distance between webs at the bottom is 6 in.

Mr. Dobert said: "The designer inspected the underside of bridge floors and noted the great amount of concrete disintegration and rust where concrete was poured next to steel.

"He proposed a completely metallic underside of his bridge floor which he obtains through the use of rolled corrugated steel box plate which can be preserved by a protective finish of paint. This complete flooring welded continuously on four sides provides the stiffness required for his horizontal floor truss."

Tees

Some T-shaped members have already been discussed under Plates. This has been true if the web or stem is very shallow, amounting to a mere stub or nose on a plate for welding, and if the edge of the stem is beveled. Some tees with short, square stems are included here.

Of all of the new shapes proposed, the new tees are the most numerous. They are used in the floor deck; as flanges for stringers, floorbeams, and longitudinal girders; as flanges of arches; as chords and diagonals of trusses; and as members of lateral bracing systems.

Mr. Forster designed the tied arch bridge shown in Figure 22 (page 64). It has trussed arches, and the chords of these arches are new tee sections that have flanges 16 in. wide and webs 16 in. deep. Also, the bracing between the arches is made of smaller new tees. Both of the new shapes are shown with dimensions in Figure 86.

His reasons for proposing these new sections are the following: "The cross section of all structural members subjected to large forces was chosen of such form as to facilitate the use of a butt weld which is the most effective connection between two steel units. Consequently, the T section was used wherever practicable, since it lends itself best to butt welding.

"Present day structural tees, which are obtained by splitting the webs of wide flange or standard I sections, have webs too thin to con-

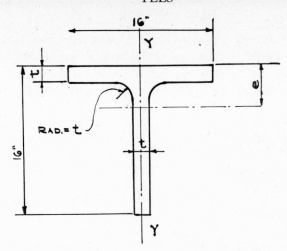

SECTION	t	WT lb.	AREA m²	I_Y	r_Y	e
16 T 1¾	1¾	184.6	54.25	605.8	3.34	4.58
16 T 1⅝	1⅝	171.8	50.49	561.4	3.33	4.54
16 T 1⅜	1⅜	146.0	42.92	474.0	3.32	4.45
16 T 1⅛	1⅛	120.0	35.28	386.1	3.30	4.37
16 T ⅞	⅞	93.8	27.56	299.6	3.29	4.29
16 T ⅝	⅝	67.3	19.78	213.7	3.28	4.20

NEW CHORD SECTION

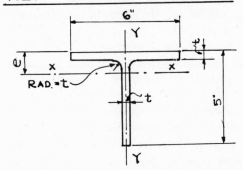

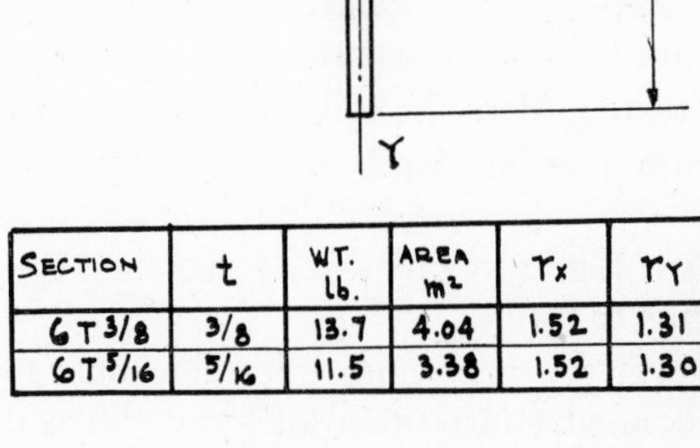

SECTION	t	WT. lb.	AREA m²	r_x	r_Y	e
6 T ⅜	⅜	13.7	4.04	1.52	1.31	1.26
6 T 5⁄16	5⁄16	11.5	3.38	1.52	1.30	1.24

NEW SECTION FOR BRACINGS.

Figure 86

form readily with the standard specifications for highway bridges requiring the width of outstanding legs not to exceed twelve times their thickness.

"To circumvent the inadequacy of current T sections, properties of special T sections were developed with web thicknesses equal to those of the flanges."

The truss Mr. Kayser designed is shown in Figure 43 (page 110). All members of the two trusses are 14 in. wide and consist of two tees welded to a web plate or to a series of tie plates. The flanges of all members are vertical and have the same thickness. These conditions eliminate eccentricities and assure a better distribution of stress at the connections. Dimensions of the new tees proposed are given in Figure 87.

Mr. Kayser commented on the fact that his truss members could be made up from plates instead of the new tees. He said: "Although the various members could be fabricated from plate, the T sections in addition to being a very flexible shape for welded design, offer the advantage of having stiffness about both axes, thus preventing dishing-in when being welded to the web, and also permitting the use of open webs or lattice-bar or tie-plate construction for some of the members, thereby reducing the weight of the structure as a whole."

As shown in Figure 15 (page 50), Mr. Akroyd designed his arch ribs using two new tees and a web plate. His stiffening girder shown in Figure 79 (page 186) consists of similar members. The floor deck, also shown in Figure 79, is a series of 9 x 2-in. tees. The details of these tees and many others are given in Figure 88.

The following is a part of Mr. Akroyd's discussion of the new sections.

"It is considered that if welding were used exclusively in fabrication such sections as angles would become redundant and would be replaced either by flats or tee sections and existing beams would be milled with parallel flanges. British practice for the production of welded plate girders is for the flange plates to be welded to the web at their junction. This is already a point of stress concentration. . . .

"In the design of plate girders, the following criteria apply:

1. The maximum possible depth for economy and strength is required.
2. Shear stresses will govern when web is less than economic depth for minimum size flange.
3. In bridge work, the maximum allowable outstanding leg of flange may be used (since the available width is unrestricted).

"The above various items have been borne in mind and a series of tees proposed on the following lines:

ROLLED "Ts" FOR WELDING *

TABLE OF AVAILABLE SIZES *

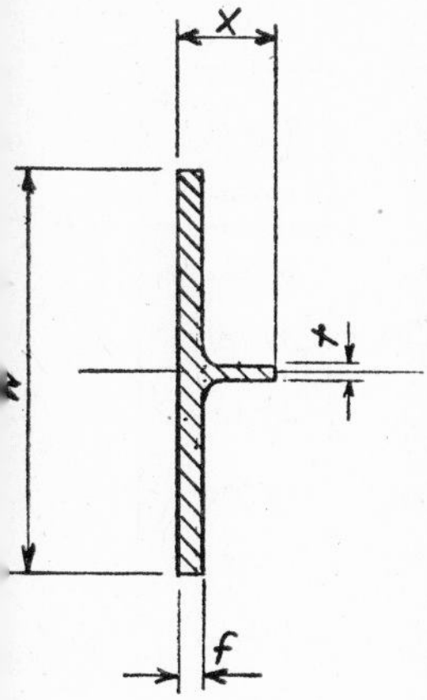

Nominal Size	W in.	f in.	t in.	x in	Area sq. in.	Weight lbs.
4"e 6.38#	4	3/8	1/4	1 7/8	1.875	6.375
5 e 7.65#	5	3/8	1/4	1 7/8	2.250	7.650
6 e 8.93*	6	3/8	1/4	1 7/8	2.625	8.925
8 e 11.48*	8	3/8	1/4	1 7/8	3.375	11.475
10 e 14.03	10	3/8	1/4	1 7/8	4.125	14.025
6 e 12.24	6 1/16	1/2	5/16	2	3.600	12.240
8 e 15.64	8 1/16	1/2	5/16	2	4.600	15.640
10 e 19.04	10 1/16	1/2	5/16	2	5.600	19.040
12 e 22.44	12 1/16	1/2	5/16	2	6.600	22.440
8 e 19.18	8 1/8	5/8	3/8	2 1/8	5.641	19.179
10 e 23.43	10 1/8	5/8	3/8	2 1/8	6.891	23.429
12 e 27.68	12 1/8	5/8	3/8	2 1/8	8.141	27.679
14 e 31.93	14 1/8	5/8	3/8	2 1/8	9.391	31.929
16 e 36.18	16 1/8	5/8	3/8	2 1/8	10.641	36.179
10 e 39.32	10 3/8	1"	5/8	2 1/2	11.563	39.314
12 e 46.12	12 3/8	1"	5/8	2 1/2	13.563	46.114
14 e 52.92	14 3/8	1"	5/8	2 1/2	15.563	52.914
16 e 59.72	16 3/8	1"	5/8	2 1/2	17.563	59.714
18 e 66.52	18 3/8	1"	5/8	2 1/2	19.563	66.514
20 e 73.32	20 3/8	1"	5/8	2 1/2	21.563	73.314
22 e 80.12	22 3/8	1"	5/8	2 1/2	23.563	80.114
24 e 86.92	24 3/8	1"	5/8	2 1/2	25.563	86.914

Assumed to be reduction.

Figure 87

1. The outstanding leg of the tee (flange part) = 12 x thickness.
2. Length of web part = 8 x thickness.
3. End of the flanges and web square cut.
4. Radius of junction of web and flange similar to that for existing tees.

"The following advantages are claimed. The sections are practical and easy to roll and will have good metallurgical properties throughout. The sections give flexibility with the advantages of standardization in the design of girders. The position of the longitudinal welds is removed from a position of high stress concentration to one of low stress."

Beams

The main variations among the new beams suggested dealt with the use of unequal flanges, adding bulbs or tips to the extremities of

New Welding Tee Sections. – Properties.

Size. A × B ins.	Wt. per ft. run. lbs.	Area per ft. run. sq. ins.	t_1 ins.	t_2 ins.	t ins.	$n. x.$ ins.	M.of I_{xx} ins.⁴	M.of I_{yy} ins.⁴
42 × 7	270.8	79.62	1.75	0.875	0.75	1.214	108.04	10704.58
39 × 7	211.0	61.95	1.625	0.875	0.75	1.191	103.81	8032.78
36 × 7	204.5	60.12	1.5	0.875	0.75	1.183	99.32	5832.0
30 × 7	148.4	43.62	1.25	0.875	0.75	1.206	94.08	2812.5
27 × 7	124.1	36.50	1.125	0.875	0.75	1.245	84.32	1849.28
24 × 7	102.2	30.12	1.0	0.875	0.75	1.312	86.26	1132.0
24 × 6	96.9	28.50	1.0	0.75	0.70	1.132	60.68	1152.0
21 × 6	77.5	22.88	0.875	0.75	0.70	1.200	55.96	675.28
21 × 5	73.2	21.50	0.875	0.625	0.70	1.011	41.42	675.28
18 × 6	61.2	18.00	0.75	0.75	0.65	1.34	48.44	365.90
18 × 5	56.6	16.62	0.75	0.625	0.65	1.101	38.05	365.90
18 × 4	52.7	15.50	0.75	0.5	0.65	0.875	26.14	365.90
15 × 5	42.5	12.50	0.625	0.625	0.65	1.292	34.20	175.78
15 × 4	38.7	11.38	0.625	0.5	0.65	0.982	23.95	175.78
15 × 3	35.7	10.50	0.625	0.375	0.65	0.720	14.51	175.78
12 × 4	27.2	8.00	0.5	0.5	0.60	1.312	21.20	72.00
12 × 3	24.2	7.12	0.5	0.375	0.60	0.980	13.41	72.00
12 × 3	23.6	6.94	0.5	0.3125	0.60	0.905	11.56	72.00
12 × 3	22.9	6.75	0.5	0.25	0.60	0.815	9.53	72.00
9 × 3	15.3	4.50	0.375	0.375	0.55	1.108	11.44	22.78
9 × 2½	14.1	4.16	0.375	0.3125	0.55	0.876	8.60	22.78
9 × 2	13.1	3.86	0.375	0.25	0.45	0.950	6.23	22.78
9 × 2	12.7	3.75	0.375	0.1875	0.45	0.552	4.52	22.78
6 × 3	11.4	3.37	0.375	0.375	0.45	1.415	10.16	6.75
6 × 2½	10.3	3.03	0.375	0.3125	0.45	1.138	7.44	6.75
6 × 2	9.3	2.75	0.375	0.25	0.45	0.856	5.57	6.75
6 × 2	8.8	2.62	0.375	0.1875	0.45	0.708	4.33	6.75

Figure 88

the flanges, or providing wider flanges in order to have the principal radii of gyration approximately equal.

Messrs. Daymond and Zakrzewski have a composite roadway floor (see Figure 71, page 171) that consists of a dished plate and a concrete slab of variable thickness. This composite floor is structurally attached to the stringers, which are new shapes that have unequal flanges, as shown in Figure 89. All stringers have top flanges that are 2½ in. wide and ½ in. thick. The exterior stringers are 14 in. deep and have bottom flanges 6 in. wide. The interior stringers are 18 in. deep and have bottom flanges 8 in. wide. The authors stated that these new sections with this type of construction results in considerable saving in steel, as evidenced by the fact that the "calculated standard rolled beam for the same condition is 50 per cent heavier."

With minor exceptions, the entire bridge designed by Mr. Rochlin is constructed out of wide flange shapes. The sizes of the members are shown in Figure 45 (page 116). Two new wide flange shapes are proposed. The first interior diagonal of the truss is a 14 WF 54 section (10 in. wide) and the diagonals of the top lateral bracing are 10 WF 30 sections (8 in. wide).

Mr. Rochlin's preference for wide flange shapes is explained in these statements included in his discussion.

"It has been one of the great advantages of welding that complicated assemblies can be made up easily out of simple elements. The ideal of welding practice would appear then to be able to make as many details as possible out of as few sections as possible. In this way welding should theoretically lead to the elimination rather than the addition of new sections.

"We must, therefore, question the value of proposing any new types of sections. This, however, does not mean that the existing sections could not be improved upon and made more adaptable to the welding process.

"The further development of welded design will lead to the greater use of wide flange sections in bridges instead of the older assemblies made up of angles, channels, and plates. It is, therefore, essential that the welding industry encourages the rolling of a larger number of these sections than is at present the case. Efforts should be made to encourage the rolling of sections which will have a larger radius of gyration around the minor axis. The designer is constantly beset by the fact that the r in one direction of the member is so much smaller than the r in the other direction. Besides this there are countless times in every designer's experience when with very low stresses a heavy member must be used simply to get the required r.

"Our proposal is to add to each wide-flange width group shown

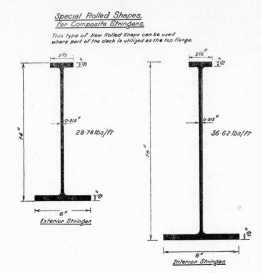

Figure 89

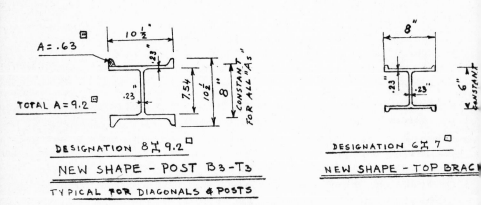

Figure 90

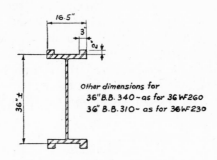

CROSS-SECTION OF PROPOSED ROLLED
"BULB BEAMS"
36 B.B. 340 and 36 B.B. 310

Figure 91

in the A.I.S.C. Manual an additional lighter section that has approximately the weight of the heaviest section in the group below. At present there is a considerable jump in this weight.

*   *   *

"It will be seen that using a 14 WF 54 instead of a 14 WF 61 which would otherwise be required to satisfy the r requirement saves 7 lb. per ft."

C. J. Kray, Reading, Massachusetts, submitted the design of a ten panel truss having non-parallel chords. For the diagonals and verticals of the truss, he proposed the larger of the two shapes shown in Figure 90. This shape varies in area from 6 sq. in. to 10.5 sq. in. The smaller shape was used for the web members of the top lateral bracing. These special shapes could be described as wide flange beams with bulbs at both ends of both flanges. The bulbs increase the moment of inertia about the axis of the web.

The larger section is 10½ in. wide and 10½ in. deep (out to out of bulbs). The smaller section is 8 in. wide and approximately 8 in. deep; however, the depth outside to outside of flanges (exclusive of the bulbs) remains a constant at 6 in. for the various areas of this size section.

In the design of his two-hinged arch, Mr. Bleich used the new shape shown in Figure 91 as the arch rib. This 36 in. section is cut horizontally and welded together forming a 48-in. deep section with hexagonal holes in the web as shown in Figure 28 (page 78).

Mr. Bleich wanted an arch rib having as large a lateral radius of gyration as possible; therefore, the material must be concentrated in the corners of the shape. He said: "To obtain such a section with a minimum of labor, a new rolled section, called 'Bulb Beam', is proposed. The shapes of the proposed rolled section is a wide flange beam with added 'bulbs', which place the material just where it does the most good. The bulbs increase the lateral radius of gyration by about 30 per cent."

Channels

Some of the many channel-shape sections that Mr. Mulder utilized in the design of his bridge are shown in Figure 34 (page 90) and Figure 77 (page 180). For the arch rib, two channels are placed together to form a rectangular profile. Rectangular sections, made also from two channels, are used for the lateral struts between the arches, for the hangers, and for the floorbeams. Again, channels welded to floor plate as longitudinal stiffeners form the same closed, rectangular section that Mr. Mulder used exclusively. The web and flanges for any given channel are equal in thickness, but this thickness varies with the web dimension.

In discussing the advantages of the rectangular members (or profiles), Mr. Mulder said:

"The following merits speak strongly to the credit of this profile.

1. A kind of standard profile has been obtained, which can very easily be produced and which may be applied for any strain [compression, tension bending, torsion].

2. As a result of point 1, a very even-tempered final construction may be anticipated, which, especially with live loads, is of very great importance. Guiding the powers [forces] through at the point where the beams meet is now effected without considerable divergence of the strains, consequently fewer strain peaks.

3. Experience has shown that painting on the inside is absolutely unnecessary.

4. A small surface to be painted, consequently less danger of corrosion.

5. No rolling strains [channels to be formed from flat plate] by the application of a profile of the same thickness everywhere.

6. As a result of the small weld, there are very slight welding

NEW SECTIONS:

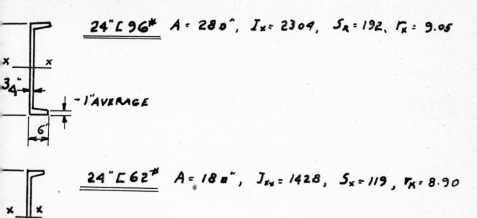

24"⊏96# A= 280", Ix= 2304, Sx= 192, rx= 9.05

- 1"AVERAGE

6'

24"⊏62# A= 180", Jxx= 1428, Sx= 119, rx= 8.90

- 3/4"AVERAGE

4 3/4"

Figure 92

strains owing to the shrinkage of the weld (also with large profiles).

7. Simple building up of the profile—consequently cheap.

8. The closing seam can be welded automatically (union melt).

9. When welding the end connections the welder need not change his position more than four times. With other profiles the welder must change his position many more times and with many profiles the welding thickness also changes, which, very often, involves much trouble.

10. The total construction acquires a smooth and massive appearance.

11. The profile can be adapted entirely to the requirements, consequently no losses owing to a profile too large having to be applied.

12. These profiles can be applied in all imaginable constructions, such as buildings, ships, cranes, etc.

"That this profile was never used with riveted construction is due to difficulties of fabrication and to the impossibility of airtight riveting."

The depth of channel shapes that Mr. Mulder has in his bridge ranges from 2½ in. up to 6 ft. and the flange width varies from 1 in. to 1 ft.-6 in.

The truss designed by Mr. Sourochnikoff has both the top chord and the bottom chord made up of two new channels each as indicated in Figure 47 (page 120). The webs of the channels are vertical and the

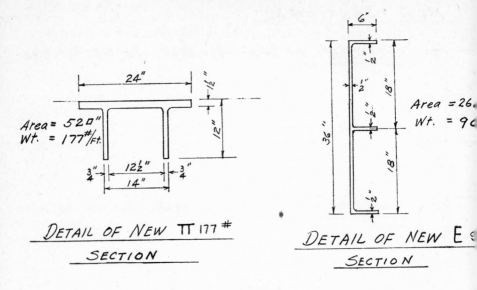

Area = 520" Wt. = 177#/Ft.

Area = 26. Wt. = 9

DETAIL OF NEW π 177#
SECTION

DETAIL OF NEW E
SECTION

Figure 93

flanges extend outward. Both of the new channels are 24 in. deep, but the top chord channels have 6-in. flanges and weigh 96 lb. per ft. whereas the bottom chord channels have 4¾-in. flanges and weigh 62 lb. per ft. The section properties and dimensions of these new channels are given in Figure 92.

In the design of his tied arch bridge (see Figure 24, page 68), Mr. Levinton used one new shape for the chords of the arch rib and another new shape as the tie. Actually, the arch rib is an open-web girder (Vierendeel truss) of variable depth. The new section for the arch chords is a channel with extensions on the web, or a tee with two stems. Mr. Levinton calls it a "Double Tee". The tie could be considered a channel with a central flange or stem. It is termed an "E" section. These new shapes are shown with dimensions in Figure 93.

The chord member is 24 in. wide and 12 in. deep. The tie member being in a vertical position is 6 in. wide and 36 in. deep. Mr. Levinton stated that the chord member "is advantageous because of its lateral strength and stability, and is suitable for carrying direct compression as well as compression combined with bending in the frame.

"In addition to its use in the present bridge design, the proposed section would also satisfy the general demand for bridge top chord members which could be built up using this section together with plates and angle. The section could be also used for box plate girders."

He anticipated the proposed E section being used for fascia beams, parapets, and flanges of plate girders. In the latter use, the web of the plate girders would be welded to the central stem of the E section. This type of construction would provide a plate girder with considerable lateral stiffness.

Angles

Few designers suggested angles different from those now available. However, Mr. Clayton is one of those who did. All of the members of his "Diamond Truss" bridge (see Figure 52, page 128) are composed of two angles arranged in a diamond configuration. He used many sizes of angles, all of which have equal legs. Two new sizes are proposed. For the chords of the truss, 18 x 18-in. angles are placed in the diamond pattern to form a closed member, and for the diagonals, 12 x 12-in. angles are so placed. Both of these sizes include a range in thickness.

Miscellaneous Shapes

Some shapes that might have been classified in this division have already been discussed. Included among these would be: the folded plate proposed by Mr. Amstutz; the IW, EW, and YW sections of Mr. Volsing; Mr. Bleich's "bulb beams"; and the "double tee" section and "E" section suggested by Mr. Levinton.

Many designers utilized large circular sections in their designs. For his arch ribs, Mr. Amstutz had tubes 3 ft. in diameter and $\frac{1}{2}$ in. thick (see Figure 25, page 72). Messrs. Gatzweiler and Kuhner used large tubes for the arch ribs and the ties in their bridge (see Figure 35, page 92). The tubes are $\frac{3}{4}$ in. thick and approximately 4 ft. in diameter. The size of tubular sections employed by other designers were smaller, but the variation in diameter and thickness was still quite large.

R. A. Close, Fairfax, Virginia, designed a tied arch. The arch ribs are trusses about 10 ft. deep. The top chord of the arch truss is a 24 WF section, but the diagonals and the bottom chord are new "cross" shapes. These shapes vary in overall dimensions from 8 in. to 24 in. The cross is used for the hangers, the ties, and the lateral bracing members. The new shape with the dimensions for the various sizes that Mr. Close proposed are shown in Figure 94.

Edward Luss, Independence, Missouri, presented the design of a prestressed bridge of the Vierendeel-truss type. The roadway deck is composed of Reliance Weldlock grating which is strengthened by special "Double Y" shapes. A larger size of this same shape is used for the cross beams. The shape is shown in Figure 95 with dimensions and properties for the different sizes. It resembles a wide flange section that has vees instead of plates for flanges.

PROPOSED NEW ROLLED SHAP

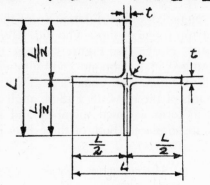

TABLE I

Symbol	L	t	Weight per foo
8"t 19.15 lb	8"	0.375"	19.15 lb
9"t 21.8 lb	9"	0.375"	21.8 lb
12"t 39.2 lb	12"	0.500"	39.2 lb
13"t 44.5 lb	13"	0.541"	44.5 lb
20"t 110 lb	20"	0.832"	110.0 lb
24"t 160 lb	24"	1.000	160.0 lb

Figure 94

DOUBLE Y PROFILE PROPERTIES

A □"	lbs	I_x	S_x	I_y	S_y	h_1	h	B	b	Δ°	t_1	t
27.73	94.4	5260	257	386	43	23	9	18	12.7	90	3/8	3/8
21.41	73.3	3152	180	182	26	21	7	14	9.9	90	5/16	3/8
20.48	70.1	2472	155	182	26	18	7	14	9.9	90	5/16	3/8
20.25	68.9	1021	98	372	39	10	5½	19	11.0	120	3/8	3/8
16.88	51.4	936	89	188	27	13	4	$13\frac{13}{16}$	8	120	3/8	3/8

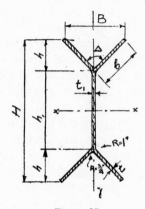

Figure 95

CHAPTER V

SPECIAL CONNECTIONS AND DETAILS

The unusual features of the primary structures and floor systems have been discussed in the preceding chapters. Even some of the special connection and arrangement details of the structure have been covered there. The purpose of this chapter is to describe a few of the new ideas for connections and details presented in this program that may be valuable to structural engineers.

It seems appropriate to recall here a small number of the special details that have been presented already. These are: the "prop" used by Messrs. Daymond and Zakrzewski (see Figure 37, page 96); Mr. Kavanagh's diagonal floorbeams and their connections (see Figures 68 and 69, pages 165 and 167); the thicker floor plate in the end panels used by Messrs. Gorgolewski and Lecewicz as the web of a horizontal girder to distribute tie load (see Figure 5 page 26 and Figure 81, page 190); the expansion connection between stringer and floorbeam presented by Messrs. Brielmaier and DeLong (see Figure 73, page 174); Mr. Forster's horizontal end trusses (see Figure 67, page 162); and the flexible end connections on Mr. Sourochnikoff's truss diagonals (see Figures 48 and 49, pages 122 and 123).

The "wedge-beams" which make up Mr. Amirikian's Vierendeel truss are shown in Figure 57 (page 137), and the end connections in Figure 58. A primary advantage of this design lies in the manner of fabrication and erection that is possible with such members. The details of the assembly and erection sequence are shown in Figure 96.

In explaining why the erection cost was estimated to be only seven per cent of the total cost of the structure, Mr. Amirikian said: "Each truss is to be erected in 6 shop-preassembled segments. As a result of the arrangement, it is possible to weld all truss joints except 15 member splices in the shop, under ideal conditions of quality control to insure safety and adequacy. Furthermore, 11 of these 15 field splices are made through butt plates, interconnected by fillet welds deposited in the horizontal position. The total amount of field welding required for the truss framing is only 196 ft., corresponding to a weld deposit of 142 lb., or about 0.7 lb. of weld per ton of steel in the trusses."

S. E. Jewkes, Perak, Malaya, designed a tied, two-hinged arch bridge. The main tie consists of a 12 x 3-in. plate and two, 6 x 1-in. bars. The bars, acting like flanges, are welded to the thick plate and form an I-shaped tie member. The tie and its end connection are shown in Figure 97. This figure shows also that the cross girders have niches at the ends where the tie member passes through. According to Mr. Jewkes, "The main tie 'floats' in niches at the ends of the cross

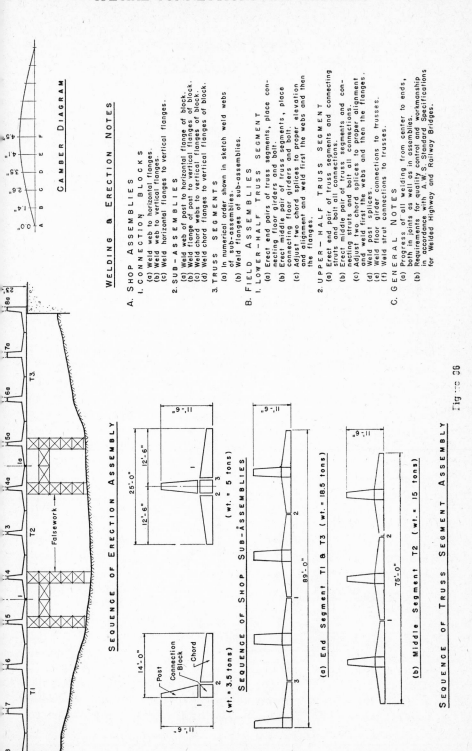

CAMBER DIAGRAM

SEQUENCE OF ERECTION ASSEMBLY

SEQUENCE OF SHOP SUB-ÁSSEMBLIES

(wt. = 3.5 tons)

(wt. = 5 tons)

(a) End Segment T1 & T3 (wt. = 18.5 tons)

(b) Middle Segment T2 (wt. = 15 tons)

SEQUENCE OF TRUSS SEGMENT ASSEMBLY

WELDING & ERECTION NOTES

A. SHOP ASSEMBLIES
  1. CONNECTION BLOCKS
    (a) Weld web to horizontal flanges.
    (b) Weld web to vertical flanges.
    (c) Weld horizontal flanges to vertical flanges.
  2. SUB-ASSEMBLIES
    (a) Weld web of post to horizontal flange of block.
    (b) Weld flange of post to vertical flanges of block.
    (c) Weld chord webs to vertical flanges of block.
    (d) Weld chord flanges to vertical flanges of block.
  3. TRUSS SEGMENTS
    (a) In numerical order shown in sketch weld webs
        of sub-assemblies.
    (b) Weld flanges of sub-assemblies.

B. FIELD ASSEMBLIES
  1. LOWER-HALF TRUSS SEGMENT
    (a) Erect end pairs of truss segments, place con-
        necting floor girders and bolt.
    (b) Erect middle pair of truss segments, place
        connecting floor girders and bolt.
    (c) Adjust two chord splices to proper elevation
        and alignment and weld first the webs and then
        the flanges.
  2. UPPER-HALF TRUSS SEGMENT
    (a) Erect end pair of truss segments and connecting
        struts and bolt all connections.
    (b) Erect middle pair of truss segments and con-
        necting struts and bolt all connections.
    (c) Adjust two chord splices to proper alignment
        and weld first the webs and then the flanges.
    (d) Weld post splices.
    (e) Weld floor girder connections to trusses.
    (f) Weld strut connections to trusses.

C. GENERAL NOTES
    (a) Progress of all welding from center to ends,
        both in joints as well as in assemblies.
    (b) Requirements for quality control and workmanship
        in accordance with A.W.S. Standard Specifications
        for Welded Highway and Railway Bridges.

Figure 36

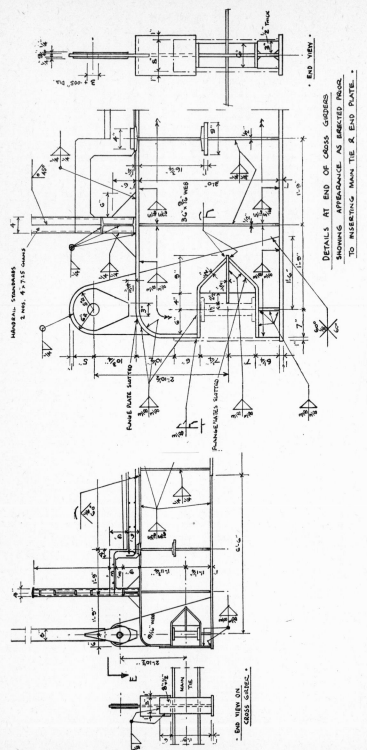

Figure 97

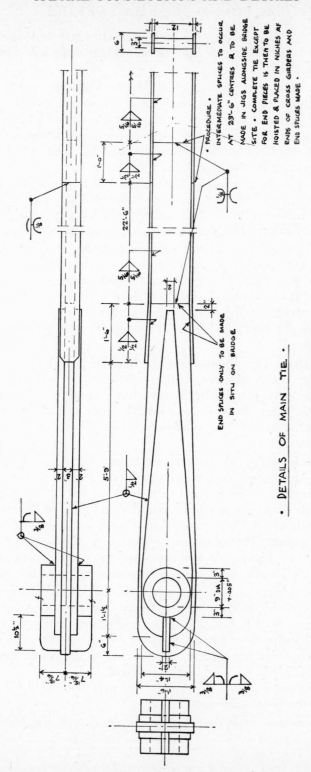

· DETAILS OF MAIN TIE. ·

Figure 97 (Concluded)

girder and is not connected to the deck until after full dead load has been applied. It is thus free to take up its natural dead load position free from restraint."

The simple welded connections that Messrs. Bretscher and Briscoe used in the design of their two-hinged arch are shown in Figures 17 and 18 (page 54 and 56). Of special interest are the steel plugs that are inserted in the ends of the four pipes at the joints of the arch rib. This splice is described in the following manner: "The sections are slipped over plugs, in the pipe in the adjoining panel, just like an erector set. The hangers fit inside the section and complete the splice. Welding of the pipe need not be done immediately, since the plugs will keep the section in line." Although the six-inch pipe could not be painted in the field, the plugs at the ends seal it against corrosion.

Mr. Rochlin stated that a principal feature of his truss bridge lies in the method of effecting the field connection at the truss joints without the use of gusset plates. The ends of the web members are cut for butt welds without coping. A plate is welded between the flanges in the shop to provide bearing for the webs on these members. Details of the truss joints are shown in Figure 46 (page 118) and discussed more fully in Chapter II.

Figure 65 (page 157) shows how Mr. Rochlin provides a moment connection for the continuous stringers that: supports the top and bottom of the stringer during construction; requires no holes in stringer or floorbeam; transfers shear directly from web of the stringer to web of floorbeam; and makes allowance for tolerance in the length of the stringer.

Single gussets of curved shape connect the pipe diagonals of Mr. Freudenthal's bridge at the bottom chord (see Figure 70 page 168) and single gussets, perpendicular to the plane of the top chord, connect these pipe diagonals at the top chord (see Figure 56, page 135). The top chords are braced by box-shaped struts only, located at the upper panel points. The struts are connected to the top chords by corner plates (see Figure 70) and thus produce a rigid frame in the plane of the top chords that transmits horizontal forces to the portals.

In order to design a two-hinged arch without lateral bracing, Mr. Bleich had to provide moment connections at both the top and bottom of all hangers (18 WF 50). The rigid connection of the floorbeam (36 WF 150) is shown in Figure 29 (page 80). In addition to welds directly between the hanger and the floorbeam, the lower moment connection includes a triangular bracket above and a 14 x ⅝-in. plate below. The upper connection between the arch rib and the hanger includes two 6 x ¾-in. splice plates.

The arch rib is a "bulb beam" 36 in. in depth that has been split

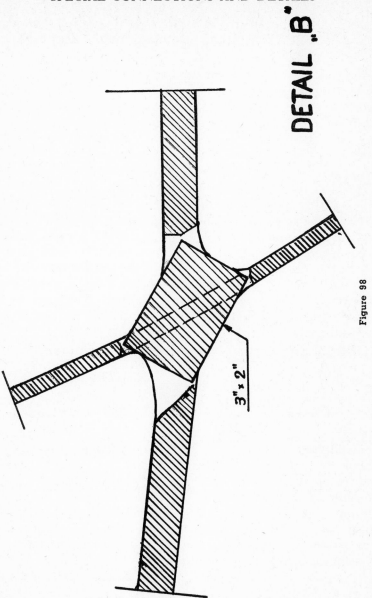

DETAIL "B"

Figure 98

3" x 2"

longitudinally and welded together, forming a section 48 in. deep. As Figure 28 shows, this section has hexagonal holes in the web.

To avoid action of the floor system as a tie for the arch, Mr. Bleich provides for expansion of the concrete deck slab and stringers at the quarter points of the span as shown in the stringer expansion detail of Figure 29. A 10-in. channel with a slotted hole is welded to each side of the reinforced web of the stringer and cantilevers across the

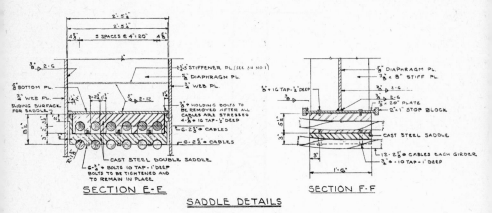

SADDLE DETAILS

SECTION E-E

SECTION F-F

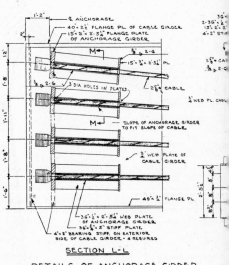

SECTION K-K

SECTION L-L

DETAILS OF ANCHORAGE GIRDER

250 FT. PRESTRES
SECTIONS AND

Figure 99

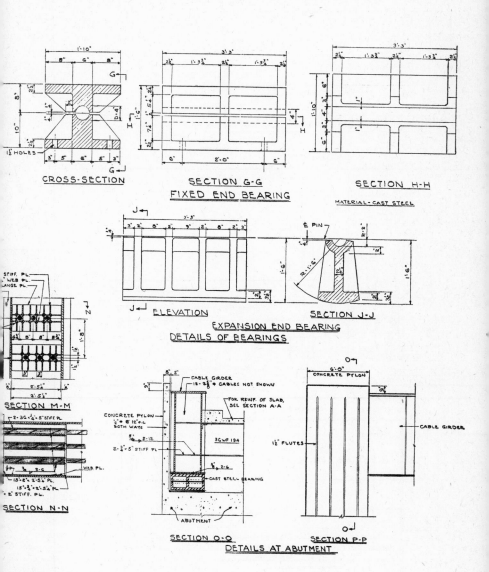

CROSS-SECTION

SECTION G·G
FIXED END BEARING

SECTION H·H

MATERIAL - CAST STEEL

STIFF. PL.
WEB PL.
FLANGE PL.

SECTION M-M

SECTION N-N

ELEVATION

EXPANSION END BEARING

DETAILS OF BEARINGS

SECTION J-J

CABLE GIRDER
12 - 2⅜" ⌀ CABLES NOT SHOWN

FOR REINF. OF SLAB,
SEE SECTION A-A

CONCRETE PYLON
½" ⌀ 6 12" O.C.
BOTH WAYS

3GWF 194

2-⅞"×5" STIFF PL

CAST STEEL BEARING

ABUTMENT

SECTION O·O

CONCRETE PYLON

1½" FLUTES

CABLE GIRDER

SECTION P-P

DETAILS AT ABUTMENT

BRIDGE
AILS

Figure 99 (Concluded)

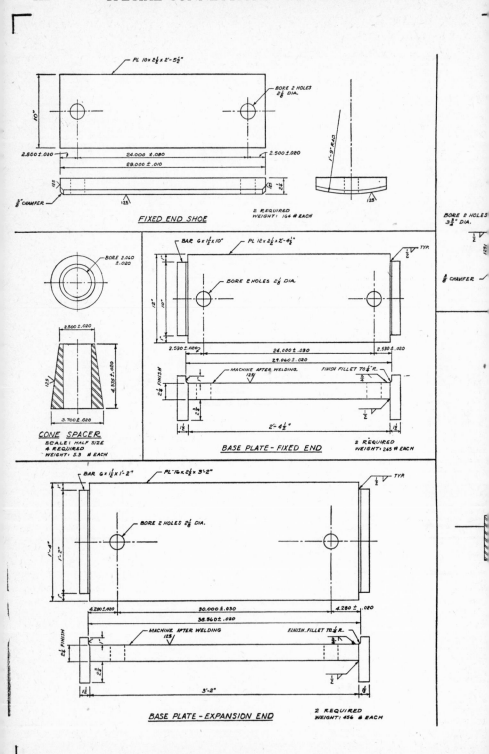

FIXED END SHOE

CONE SPACER

BASE PLATE - FIXED END

BASE PLATE - EXPANSION END

Figure 100

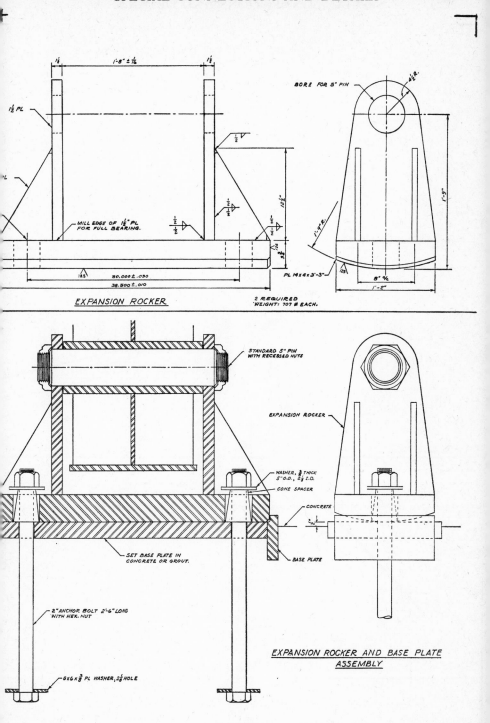

EXPANSION ROCKER

2 REQUIRED
WEIGHT: 707 # EACH.

BORE FOR 5" PIN

PL 14x4x3'-3"

MILL EDGE OF 1½" PL
FOR FULL BEARING.

STANDARD 5" PIN
WITH RECESSED NUTS

EXPANSION ROCKER

WASHER, ⅜ THICK
5" O.D., 2⅛ I.D.
CONE SPACER

CONCRETE

SET BASE PLATE IN
CONCRETE OR GROUT.

BASE PLATE

2" ANCHOR BOLT 2'-6" LONG
WITH HEX. NUT

6x6x⅜ PL WASHER, 2⅛ HOLE

EXPANSION ROCKER AND BASE PLATE
ASSEMBLY

Figure 100 (Concluded)

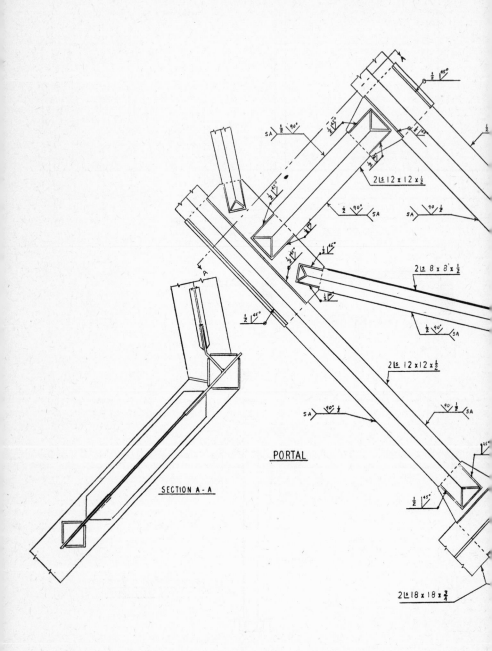

PORTAL

SECTION A - A

Figure 101

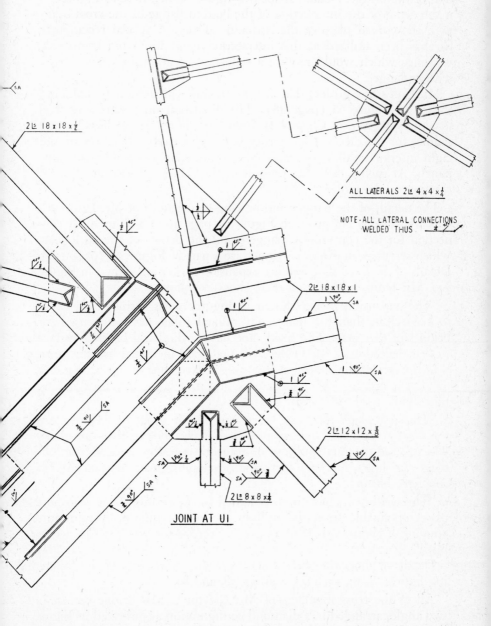

JOINT AT UI

Figure 101 (Concluded)

floorbeam. The adjacent stringer is attached to the extended channels by inserting a 2-in. pin through the slotted holes.

Mr. Amstutz has one stiffening girder of semi-circular shape for his two-hinged arch bridge. Figure 26 (page 74) shows a transverse section of the bridge. Detail "B" of this figure, shown here as Figure 98, is the detail of the intersection of the bottom flange of the cross beam with the curved plate of the stiffening girder. A special rectangular bar has been utilized at this intersection point to "avoid transversal weldings which would require a reduction of allowable stress in the tension flange."

Mr. Coff's box girders that are prestressed with tensional cables are shown in Figure 62 (page148). His discussion on prestressing steel structures is given in Chapter II. Figure 99 shows the anchorages and saddles for the cables. Each girder has twelve cables stretched around eight interior saddles; therefore, the 250-ft. span is divided into nine panels. At each saddle, the tension in the cables produce an upward reaction on the girder.

The details of the hanger and bracing connections of Mr. Jennison's tied arch bridge are given in Figure 2 (page 16). The moment connection for the continuous stringers and the details of the curb plate which serves as an exterior stringer are a part of Figure 66 (page 158). Details of the fixed shoe and the expansion rocker are shown in Figure 100. Mr. Jennison discussed these shoes as follows:

"The expansion rocker shown in Figure 100 is simpler and easier to keep clean than the more conventional roller nest often used for bridges of this span. The fixed shoe has a cylindrical bearing surface so that deflection of the bridge will not cause increased bearing stress near the face of the abutment. By using a fixed shoe of the same radius as the expansion rocker, the same set-up in a lathe of vertical boring mill can be used to machine the radius.

"The base plates are to be set in concrete or grout for bearing and for shear resistance. Lugs are provided at the ends of the base plates, which serve the dual purpose of transmitting lateral force from the rocker or shoe to the base plate and developing shear resistance in the concrete abutment.

"The weldments have been designed for fabrication from slabs and plates obtainable from the mill in the sizes required. A minimum amount of shop work is necessary to prepare for welding the assemblies."

Details of shoes for other designs are shown as parts of the following figures: 8, 14, 15, 23, 37, 46, 64, 78, and 80.

All of the truss members of Mr. Clayton's truss bridge consist of two angles arranged in a diamond configuration as indicated in Figure

52 (page 128). The top and bottom lateral bracing and the handrail members have the same shape. As shown in Figure 101, this type of section permits the use of single gusset plates at the connections.

Mr. Clayton said: "It is believed that these joints possess the following characteristics:

1. The strength of the joint is equal to, or greater than the strength of the weaker of the members joined.
2. Joining of members can be accomplished without producing distortion due to strains introduced by welding.
3. Accomplishes the desired results with the use of a minimum of deposited metal.
4. Permits branch joints without the use of complicated designs.
5. Has pleasing appearance.
6. Allows accurate positioning of members joined.

CHAPTER VI
QUANTITIES AND COSTS

In compliance with the requirements of the Rules and Conditions, each exhibit of this program contained an estimate of the cost of the design, a table giving the total quantity of steel required, and a table giving the total quantity of the welds required. The various steel sections were listed separately according to size and shape, and similarly, the different sizes and types of shop welds and field welds were itemized separately.

The information presented here has been taken from a few of the designs submitted to show the total weights of some of the bridges, the relative weights of the different parts of the structure, and the relationship between the amount of welding and the amount of steel. In addition to weights and quantities, unit costs and total costs as estimated by the designers are given. It is well known that costs have been changing quite rapidly in recent years, and also, that the cost of a specified structure at any given time will vary from one country to another, or even within the same country. Consequently, in comparing the cost information, it will be necessary to consider these normal variations and realize that the values given were the best estimates of the authors at the time their designs were submitted.

Mr. Jennison included elaborate tables of welding costs and unit material costs for his tied arch bridge(see Figure 1, page 14), but they are too lengthy to be presented here. A summary of the steel quantities is given in Table 1, and a cost estimate summary in Table 2. About the materials required and the cost of fabrication and construction, Mr. Jennison said:

"The amount of steel required for this tied arch bridge with a stiffening tie girder is fairly low for a simply supported span, but it is probably about the same as the amount required for a well designed welded truss bridge with a deck of the same weight. Less structural steel would be required if a lightweight type of deck were used. However, the total cost for a bridge of this span would be greater because of the more expensive deck. The dead load of the deck is 2600 lb. per ft. and the total dead load 4147 lb. per ft.

"The materials required are summarized in Table 1. The total weight of structural steel excluding expansion rockers, shoes, and base plates is 376,107 lb. This is 58 lb. per sq. ft., compared to 75-90 lb. of structural steel per sq. ft. for riveted bridges of equal span. Using an estimating formula [see L. C. Urquhart and C. E. O'Rourke, *Design of Steel Structures,* McGraw-Hill Book Company, p. 340, 1930] for computing the weight of the trusses, and designing the stringers as simple spans, the weight of steel required for a riveted through truss bridge is estimated to be 480,000 lb. From these comparisons, it is evident that an equivalent riveted bridge would require 28 to 55 per cent more structural steel than the welded bridges.

"The costs of fabrication and construction are influenced by many factors including economic conditions, competition, efficiency of the contractor's organization, transportation cost, and the local conditions at the construction site. In arriving at a cost estimate, the author has assumed average conditions and has made general allowance for the cost of falsework and steel erection. Only under extremely adverse conditions, should the cost be expected to run higher.

"All costs were estimated by a detailed analysis of labor and materials required for each operation. This method is more reliable than any other for a structure such as this one which differs significantly from usual design. Only with accumulated experience in fabrication and erection of similar welded bridges could a contractor safely estimate the job on the basis of unit prices without detailed analysis.

"The author's estimates are based on current Los Angeles prices and

Table 1

Summary of Structural Steel

Item	Weight in Pounds
Arch Rib	77,582
Stringers	35,278
Floorbeams	69,426
Tie Girder	122,489
Curb	32,535
Hangers and Bracing	38,797
Shoes and Bearings	4,125
Railings	9,380
Anchor Bolts, Washers, Pins	707
Total Structural Steel	390,319
Reinforcing Steel for Deck Slab	30,866
Total Steel	421,185
Concrete in Deck Slab	152.5 cu. yd.

Table 2.

COST ESTIMATE SUMMARY

Structural Steel: 341,308 lb. @ $0.055	$ 18,772
Flame-Cutting and Bevelling	395
Misc. Shop Costs, Including Layout, Handling, Galvanizing Deck Joint Assemblies, Bending Rib Flanges at U_1, U_3, and U_5, and Bending Curb Plates	2,923
Shop Welding	1,091
Field Welding	2,037
Platforms or Staging for Welders and Painters	2,000
Temporary Falsework, Including Erection and Removal	6,500
Steel Erection, Including Equipment Costs	6,100
Pins and Pin Nuts for Expansion Rocker	600
Milling Ends of Stiffeners	50
Boring Pin Holes in Rockers and Girder Bearing	150
Machining Rockers and Shoes	1,000
Planing Base Plates	500
Anchor Bolts, Washers, Spacers, etc.	150
Pipe, Black Steel	
2 in. Standard: 505 lin ft @ $0.35	177
6 in. Standard: 543 lin ft @ $1.50	815
8 in. Standard: 1,154 lin ft @ $2.00	2,310
Tubing, Square and Rectangular: 7,540 lb. @ $0.10	754
Reinforcing Steel, in Place: 30,866 lb. @ $0.08	2,470
Concrete, in Place: 152.5 cu yd @ $18.00	2,750
Forms, Including Material, Labor, and Stripping	2,410
Painting, 3 Coats on 29,000 sq ft	
Paint: 171 gal @ $4.50	770
Labor:	5,680
Total, Including Overhead at 100% of Direct Labor	$ 60,404
Contingencies: 10%	6,040
Subtotal	$ 66,444
Profit: 15%	9,966
Total Cost of Superstructure	$ 76,410

Cost per square ft $= \dfrac{\$76,410}{252 \times 26} = \$11.65$ per square ft.

Unit Prices of Materials in Place Derived From Above Estimate
    (a) Including Overhead, 100% of Direct Labor.
    (b) Including Contingencies, 10% of Total Cost.
    (c) Including Profit, 15% of Cost Including Contingencies.

Steel, Structural, Excluding Rockers, Shoes, and Base Plates:

$$\frac{\$63,720}{385,487} = \$0.165 \text{ per lb.}$$

Concrete, in Place, Including Forms: $\dfrac{\$6,526}{152.5} = \$42.80$ per cu. yd.

Reinforcing Steel, in Place: $0.08 per lb.

wage rates. Mill order rather than warehouse prices of steel are assumed.

"Although the cost of pipe per lb. is higher than the cost of rolled shapes, the savings in weight, more desirable appearance, and general suitability of the pipe members justify the higher cost per lb. The advantages of pipe for structural members will result in savings in overall cost, and pipe should be used more often for structural members."

Mr. Jennison computed the weight of shop welds to be 365 lb. and field welds to be 518 lb. The estimated costs of the welds were $1091 for the shop welds and $1959 for the field welds.

Mr. Amstutz used a folded steel plate filled with concrete and topped with macadam as the deck for his two-hinged arch bridge (see Figure 25, page 72). The quantities of materials for this bridge are listed in Table 3. Of the total of 484,365 lb. of steel, plates accounted for 337,452 lb. and wide-flange sections for 47,392 lb. The total weight of shop welds is 2,841 lb. and the total weight of field welds is 1,390 lb.

As part of his exhibit, Mr. Kavanagh presented the comparison of weights of five designs. One is the welded bridge entered in this program. The other four are bridges having riveted connections, but are designed for the same span, loading, and specifications as the welded bridge. All five bridges have 6 in. of concrete slab plus wearing surface;

Table 3

Summary of Quantities

Item	Weight in Pounds
Roadway Floor (Steel)	194,250
Curbs	48,300
Cross Girders	49,616
Longitudinal Girder	67,124
Hangers	6,908
Arches	104,564
Railings	6,203
Bearings (Cast Steel)	7,400
Total Steel	484,365
Concrete in Floor	38 cu. yd.
Macadam or Asphalt Surface	41 cu. yd.

FOR DETAIL SEE REPORT

COMPARATIVE WEIGHTS (TONS)

STRUCTURAL STEEL

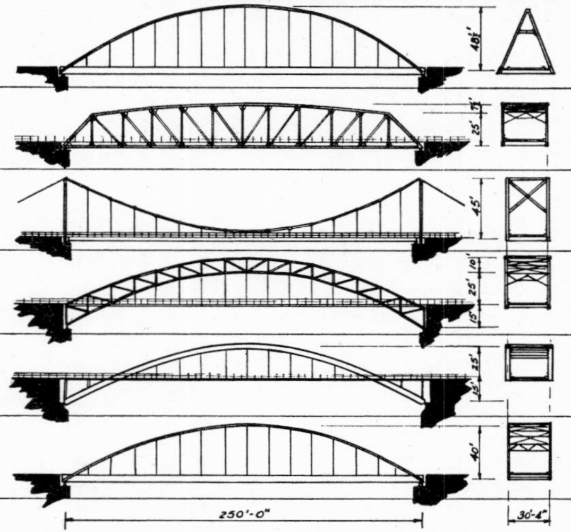

ELEVATIONS (SCALE 1" = 60')
250'-0"
30'-4"

	BRIDGE TYPE	MAIN STRUCTURE	BRACING	FLOORING	MISCEL.	TOTAL STEEL
WELDED	THIS DESIGN	127.3	2.6	50.0	2.2	182.1
RIVETED	SIMPLE TRUSS	160.9	30.5	79.6	8.0	279.0
RIVETED	EYEBAR SUSPENSION BRIDGE	173.2	10.0	74.1	10.0	267.2
RIVETED	2-HINGED BRACED ARCH RIB	113.4	31.1	87.6	8.0	240.1
RIVETED	2-HINGED SOLID ARCH RIB	163.0	20.0	87.6	8.0	278.6
RIVETED	TIED ARCH - SLENDER RIB	150.7	22.5	74.1	3.0	250.3
RIVETED	DO. - ST. GEORGES SPAN (540' SPAN)	64%	9%	23%	4%	100%

Figure 102

however, the welded bridge has the diagonal gridwork of stringers as shown in Figure 3 (page 20), whereas the riveted bridges have the conventional stringer-floorbeam arrangement. Figure 102 shows the summary of the weights of each bridge.

A summary of the weights for Mr. Kavanagh's welded bridge is given in Table 4. This tied arch required 2,953 lb. of deposited weld metal for shop welds and 730 lb. for field welds. The total weight of welds of 3,683 lb. is at the limit of one per cent of the weight of the steel, which Mr. Kavanagh indicated as a desirable maximum given by R. G. Braithwaite and D. J. Davies in "Welded Highway Bridges" (*Journal of the Institute of Civil Engineers,* London, April 1950, No. 6, p. 109).

Table 4

Summary of Weights

Item	Weight in Pounds
Arch Ribs	101,158
Tie Girders	146,130
Hangers	7,410
Bracing	5,270
Flooring (Structural Steel)	99,850
Bearings	4,332
Total Steel	364,150

Ttl. Flooring Weight—Concrete—Per Ft. of Bridge = 3625 lb.
Ttl. Flooring Weight—Stringers—Per Ft. of Bridge = 396 lb.
Ttl. Structural Steel Per Ft. of Bridge = 1455 lb.

In discussing costs and comparative economy, Mr. Kavanagh said: "Summarizing European experience, two English writers [see Braithwaite and Davies reference] cite savings of 18 to 22 per cent possible in the case of welded arch bridges. A recent digest of Australian experience [see V. Karmalsky, 'Australia's Welded Highway Bridges' *Engineering News-Record,* June 1, 1950, p. 39] indicates a general savings of 20 per cent by weight with all-welded construction.

"The design submitted produces steel weight reductions of from 24 to 35 per cent in comparison with five other designs submitted. This does not tell the whole story, however, for there is a 'hidden bonus' in the way of the automatic inclusion of sidewalks in the subject design, not provided for in the comparative bridges.

"With reference to monetary savings, as is pointed out in the Braithwaite and Davies article, the cost of laying down a weld in terms of stress transmitted is no more than that of driving the corresponding rivets. A 3-in. length of ¼-in. fillet weld will carry as much shear as a ¾-in. rivet, and the cost of laying down this amount of weld will correspond to the cost of drilling holes and heating and driving the rivet. There are, of course many instances where sufficient 'production' and repetitive operations may lower the costs of welding, and there are certainly other factors, such as lower equipment costs which

Table 5

Summary of Weights

Item	Weight in Pounds
Dished Plates	66,880
Stringers	30,176
Cross Girders	39,056
Edge Plate Assemblies	21,077
Railing	10,656
Curbs	14,289
Total for Deck	182,134
Arch Ribs	136,408
Props	37,638
Hangers and Fittings	16,463
Reinforcing Steel	6,329
Miscellaneous	4,251
Welding	2,448
Total Structural Steel	385,671
Cast Steel for Clevis and Turnbuckle	5,320
Cast Iron for Drains	650
Aluminum for Gutter	144
Lead	70
Bronze	6
Wire Mesh	1,430

Table 6

Summary of Weights

Item	Weight in Pounds
Corrugated Floor	69,258
Floorbeams	57,500
Stringers and Clip Angles	107,945
Curb	36,514
Total Floor System	271,217
Truss and Bracing Members	233,650
Connection Plates	53,617
Total Steel	558,484

favor welding; on the other hand there are factors in connection with field connections which may favor the riveted procedure (enough, at least, to prompt the Australian's [see V. Karmalsky reference] to adopt shop-welded, field-riveted construction for all their steel bridges)."

Messrs. Daymond and Zakrzewski computed the total steel weight for their arch bridge (see Figure 36, page 94) is 385,671 lb. including the welds. The shop welds weigh 1816 lb. and the field welds 632 lb. Table 5 is a summary of weights for steel and other materials except concrete and asphalt. A total of 79 cu. yd. of concrete and 29 cu. yard of asphalt are required.

Messrs. Brielmaier and DeLong gave the following percentages for the weights of the various parts of their three-hinged arch bridge with its open grating deck (see Figure 30, page 83):

Grid Flooring and Sills	28%
Stringers	11
Floorbeams	9
Arches, Hangers, and Stiffening Girders	40
Bracing	6
Shoes, Railing, and Miscellaneous	6
	100%

Mr. Kayser's truss is shown in Figure 43 (page 110). The floor system has a 3½-in. corrugated plate filled with asphalt as a deck surface. The steel weights are given in Table 6. The shop welds required amount to 3,847 lb. and the field welds 1,197 lb. The weight of the asphalt paving is listed as 355,625 lb. The cost summary is as follows:

Fabricated Structural Steel	$ 58,000
Erection	32,800
Asphalt Paving	800
	$ 91,600
Administration, Overhead, and Insurance	$ 18,400
	$110,000
Profit	$ 11,000
TOTAL	$121,000

Mr. Rochlin computed the weights for his truss bridge (see Figure 45, page 116) including its reinforced concrete roadway as follows:

	Main Members	Small Pieces	Total
Trusses	225,725	4,687	230,412
Floor System & Exp. Jts.	129,399	11,720	141,119
Handrail	22,604	1,617	24,221
Bottom Chord Bracing	8,080	241	8,321
Upper Chord Bracing, Portal & Sway Bracing	37,722	1,198	38,920
Bearings	. . . . . .	6,894	6,894
TOTAL	423,530	26,357	449,887

To this total of 449,887 lb. of structural steel, he added 560 lb. of shop welds, 660 lb. of field welds, and 1,804 lb. for shop paint (0.4 per cent allowance). The reinforcing steel for the 189 cu. yd. of concrete weighs 30,000 lb. He estimated the cost of steel, including erection, to be $230 per ton.

Mr. Amirikian included in his exhibit very complete tables of costs of cutting, edge preparation and welding. The summary of steel weights for Vierendeel truss is as follows:

Member	Weight in Pounds
2 Trusses	418,000
11 Girders	38,610
11 Struts	19,120
80 Stringers	84,630
20 Railing Panels	4,000
Splices and Connection Plates	200
Slab Anchorage	4,240
Foundation Plates and Anchors	2,800
TOTAL	571,600

The weight of electrodes, including waste, is 10,620 lb. for shop welds and 360 lb. for field welds. Of the 10,620 lb., 1,961 lb. is used for the welding of the "wedge" beams (see Figure 57, page 137). The field welds amount to only 0.063 per cent of the total steel weight.

Table 7 shows the main breakdown of the total cost. The roadway flooring consists of precast and prestressed concrete panels. The quantity of concrete is 106 cu. yd.

Figure 79 (page 186) shows a cross section of Mr. Akroyd's arch bridge with its unusual floor system. The cost estimate for the bridge was $96,600. This allows $90,480 for the 594,000 lb. of structural steel, $3520 for the concrete and asphalt, and $2600 for 4 coats of paint. The steel summary is as follows:

Tee Sections of Flooring	137,800 lb.
Cross Girders	132,600
Stiffening Girders	131,100
Arch	172,100
Cross Bracing	10,100
Hanger Rods	10,300
	594,000 lb.

The shop welds weigh 4097 lb. and the field welds 1392 lb. for a total of 5,489 lb.

In the design of his tied arch (see Figure 13, page 44), Mr. Arild used pipe sections for the arch, the lateral bracing, and the stiffening truss; consequently, out of a total of 380,800 lb. of steel, pipes account for 148,216 lb. The cables weigh 25,367 lb. and the cast steel anchor heads weigh 8,791 lb. To this low structural steel weight should be added 39,000 lb. of reinforcement steel for the 189 cu. yd. of concrete for the roadway slab. For this bridge, the shop welds amount to 1290 lb. and the field welds to 840 lb.

The tied arch bridge designed by Messrs. Gorgolewski and Lecewicz is shown in Figure 5 (page 76). Their summary of steel is given in Table 8. The 507,123 lb. of steel require 6003 lb. of shop welds and 1683 lb. of field welds.

In addition to the floor plate which is included in the structural

---

Table 7

Total Costs

Steel Framework		
Steel, f.o.b. mill		$21,677
Transportation & Handling		8,605
Fabrication:		
Preparation	$2,138	
Shop Welding	4,202	
Painting	5,040	
		$11,380
Erection:		
Falsework	$1,500	
Assembly	1,560	
Field Welding	358	
		$ 3,418
		$45,070
Concrete Work		
Roadway Slab	$6,660	
Sidewalk Slab	480	
		$ 7,140
		$52,210
Profit and Contingencies		$10,790
TOTAL COST		$63,000

Table 8

Summary of Steel

Item	Weight in Pounds
Arch Ribs	117,844
Wind Bracing	24,752
Hangers	7,760
Floor Plate with Sub-Stringers	140,327
Stiffening Girders	99,702
Floorbeams	27,972
Cross Beams	26,022
Outside Stringers	29,964
Railing and Curb	20,008
Bearings and Expansion Joints	12,772
Total Steel	507,123

Table 9

Estimated Cost

Item	Rate	Quantity	Cost
Erected Steelwork	$388 per ton*	181.2 tons*	$70,200
Slab Reinforcement	$152 per ton*	26.7 tons*	$ 4,000
Concrete for Slab	$ 20 per cu. yd.	159 cu. yd.	$ 3,180
Asphalt	$6.70 per sq. yd.	740 sq. yd.	$ 4,950
Sand Blasting & Painting			$15,000
			$97,330

* Long Tons

steel, a total of 22,200 lb. of reinforcing steel and 88 cu. yd. of concrete is necessary for the roadway deck.

Mr. Hamilton's tied arch bridge is shown in Figure 7 (page 30). The roadway is a reinforced concrete slab, 7 in. thick, topped with 1½ in. of asphalt. It requires 58,000 lb. of reinforcing steel, 159 cu. yd. of concrete, and 740 sq. yd. of asphalt paving. The structural steel has a total weight of 405,919 lb. This weight includes 10,801 lb. for handrails and 4,732 lb. for bearings, but it does not include the 1634 lb. of shop welds and 565 lb. of field welds. Table 9 is Mr. Hamilton's estimated cost of the bridge.